**Ciba Foundation
Study Group No. 18**

BRAIN–THYROID
RELATIONSHIPS

Ciba Foundation Study Groups

Ciba Foundation
Study Group
No. 18

Brain–Thyroid Relationships

with special reference to thyroid disorders

In honour of Professor S. Artunkal

Edited by Margaret P. Cameron, M.A.
and
Maeve O'Connor, B.A.

With 28 Illustrations

1964

LITTLE, BROWN AND

COMPANY

BOSTON

The purpose of the Ciba Foundation, which is to promote international co-operation in medical and chemical research, is symbolized in the armorial bearings by five interlaced rings representing the continents, a sacrificial cock (emblem of Aesculapius) holding a medical caduceus, and three regular hexagons for chemistry. Its domicile in London is indicated by the sword of St. Paul and the British lion; the wyvern and the crozier, symbols associated with Basle, refer to the sponsoring firm located in this ancient Swiss town.

Library of Congress Catalog Card No.: 64–22570

Preface

The *Ciba Foundation*, a unique international institution, owes its inception to the generosity of CIBA Limited, Basle. However, being established under British trust law, it enjoys complete independence in practice and policy.

Under the guidance of its distinguished Trustees, the Foundation offers accommodation to scientists from all over the world at its home in Portland Place. Foremost in its activities is the organization of small conferences, some lasting three or four days, others for one day only. The proceedings of the former are published in book form, and the latter in the manner of the present booklet. Each of these one-day study groups is being organized in honour and around the work of an eminent member of the Foundation's scientific advisory panel, on which there are one or more representatives for most of the countries of the world.

The Foundation convenes many other informal discussions between research workers of different disciplines and different nationalities and each year invites an outstanding authority to deliver a special lecture. An exchange programme between French and British postgraduates is conducted and a library service is available. Furthermore, the Ciba Foundation attempts in every other way possible to aid scientists, whether they be Nobel Laureates or young graduates making their first original contribution to research.

It is hoped that the rapid publication of these study groups in a compact form and at a popular price will permit readers in more distant centres, away from easy reference to the latest literature, to feel more closely in touch with recent developments, many of which have important clinical significance, and be stimulated to make their own topical contributions to international research.

Contents

Membership

Study Group on Brain—Thyroid Relationships, 16th January, 1964

B. Andersson .	.	Kungl. Veterinärhögskolan, Stockholm
S. Artunkal .	.	Dept. of Pharmacology and Therapeutics, University of Istanbul
R. A. J. Asher .	.	Central Middlesex Hospital, London
K. Brown-Grant	.	Dept. of Human Anatomy, University of Oxford
J. T. Eayrs .	.	Dept. of Neuroendocrinology, Institute of Psychiatry, The Maudsley Hospital, London
W. H. Florsheim	.	U.S. Veterans' Administration Hospital, Long Beach, California, and Los Angeles Medical School, University of California
J. G. Gibson .	.	Dept. of Mental Health, Belfast City Hospital, Belfast
Raymond Greene	.	Royal Northern Hospital and New End Hospital, London
G. W. Harris .	.	Dept. of Human Anatomy, University of Oxford
E. H. Jellinek .	.	Maida Vale Hospital, London
Sir Aubrey Lewis	.	Institute of Psychiatry, The Maudsley Hospital, London
B. M. Mandelbrote .		Littlemore Hospital, Oxford
J. Money .	.	Office of Psychohormonal Research, The Johns Hopkins Hospital, Baltimore
Joan W. Reeves	.	Dept. of Psychology, Bedford College, London
S. Reichlin .	.	Endocrine Unit, University of Rochester School of Medicine and Dentistry, Rochester, N.Y.
D. Richter .	.	Neuropsychiatric Research Unit, M.R.C. Laboratories, Carshalton
H. R. Rollin .	.	Horton Hospital, Epsom, and Nuffield College, Oxford
A. W. Spence .	.	Dept. of Medicine, St. Bartholomew's Hospital, London
W. A. H. Stevenson		Dept. of Psychological Medicine, St. Bartholomew's Hospital, London
Beglan Toğrol .	.	Dept. of Psychology, University of Istanbul

CHAIRMAN'S OPENING REMARKS

DR. RAYMOND GREENE

FIRST I would like to welcome Professor Artunkal. I am not only pleased but proud to see him, because many years ago he was a postgraduate student of mine and like all good students he has long since passed his master.

One of the important things about this meeting is that it will enable some of us to pass out of what is called, in a somewhat pejorative way, the anecdotal stage of the study of brain-thyroid relationships. It is really rather unfair to regard the word "anecdotal" as pejorative, because every study has to go through a process of making observations, before the observations can be welded together into a solid piece of knowledge. Everybody has known for a long time that there is a relationship between thyroid function and the workings of the mind, but I think that our knowledge has been held back very largely by difficulties of diagnosis. To give you one example of how people may differ from one another in diagnosis, you will remember that some years ago Dr. Asher wrote a paper which I am glad to say he did not call "Certain psychoses commonly associated with debased intra-cellular oxygen utilization", but "Myxoedematous madness" (1949. *Brit. med. J.*, **2,** 555), and because he used this less pompous phraseology the idea that myxoedematous people could be completely mad at last got through to the medical world. In spite of this, after the publication of his paper there was a spate of letters from eminent individuals completely denying that such a condition existed. Of course, those of us who have interested ourselves in both psychiatry and endocrinology know perfectly well that it does exist, and I have for a long time been advocating a survey of all the mental hospitals in the country. I am sure that in many of them a large number of people suffering from treatable endocrine disorders would be found and the commonest of all would be people suffering from hypothyroidism. I think that we are beginning to realize now that an enormous number of hypo-thyroid patients go undiagnosed because they do not conform to the usual textbook description of the fat, pale, middle-aged woman with a malar flush, cold skin, slow movements and a slow mind. We now know that just one of the various classical signs and symptoms of this disorder should give us a hint, and now that we have rather more accurate methods of investigation than the basal metabolic rate, it is possible to pick out a very large number of patients who are quite definitely hypothyroid, though not obviously so. The range of our study of the relationship between hypothyroidism and the mind can be enormously extended in consequence—we do not have to confine it to the classical type of myxoedema.

We have enough clinical information now to pass from the anecdotal stage of fact-collecting to that of welding these observations together, and some of those people who have been most prominent in this process of welding are with us here. I hope that the physiologists will remember that there are doctors in the house, and will try not to take up the whole time. I would like to hear a lot from the clinicians as well as the physiologists.

A SUMMARY OF SOME RECENT RESEARCH ON BRAIN-THYROID RELATIONSHIPS

G. W. HARRIS

Department of Human Anatomy, University of Oxford

DATA relating the central nervous system to anterior pituitary thyrotropin (TSH) secretion, and therefore to thyroid function, are of relatively recent origin. Although the effect of anterior pituitary secretion of thyrotropic hormone (TSH) on the thyroid gland has been known since the work of Allen (1916), Smith (1916, 1927), and Loeb and Bassett (1929), the neural mechanisms controlling the release of TSH had been investigated little until the last ten years. It is not the purpose of this introductory paper to review the wide field concerning the control of TSH secretion, but rather to summarize in a general way what facts we know and to outline what seem to be important gaps in our knowledge. Important reviews with full references to past and current literature are available (D'Angelo, 1963; Brown-Grant, 1964).

The two main factors known to be important in regulating TSH secretion are: (1) Hypothalamic control of anterior pituitary thyrotropic function, and (2) the feedback action of thyroxine (T_4) in the circulating blood.

HYPOTHALAMIC CONTROL OF TSH SECRETION

The fact that the hypothalamus is intimately concerned with the regulation of TSH secretion is shown by several types of experimental procedures.

Firstly, the separation of the anterior pituitary gland from the influence of the hypothalamus (by effective pituitary stalk section) results in a lowered basal secretion of TSH under resting and optimum conditions (Brolin, 1945, 1947; Donovan and Harris, 1956; Brown-Grant, Harris and Reichlin, 1957), and also a loss of reflex alteration of TSH secretion by such stimuli as cold and emotional stress (Uotila, 1939, 1940; Brolin, 1945, 1947; Brown-Grant, Harris and Reichlin, 1957). Pituitary transplantation away from the site of the hypothalamus also results in reduced basal function of the thyroid gland (Harris and Jacobsohn, 1952; Greer, Scow and Grobstein, 1953; Scow and Greer, 1955; Goldberg and Knobil, 1957; Nikitovitch-Winer and Everett, 1958; Martini *et al.*, 1959; Knigge, 1961), although transplantation into the subarachnoid space, where the tissue becomes vascularized by the hypophysial portal vessels, maintains a more normal thyroid morphology (Harris and Jacobsohn, 1952) and thyroid function (Nikitovitch-Winer and Everett, 1958, 1959). The reflex activation of TSH secretion by a cold stimulus does not occur if the pituitary has been transplanted away from its normal site (von Euler and Holmgren, 1956*b*; Knigge and Bierman, 1958).

Lesions, especially in the supraoptic region of the hypothalamus, have been shown by many workers to result in depression of various indices of thyroid function, reflecting depression in TSH secretion (Cahane and Cahane, 1936, 1938; Greer, 1951, 1952; Bogdanove and Halmi, 1953; Greer and Erwin, 1954; Bogdanove, Spirtos and Halmi, 1955; Ganong, Frederickson and Hume, 1955; D'Angelo and Traum, 1956, 1958; Olivecrona, 1957; D'Angelo, 1958; Florsheim, 1958; Reichlin, 1960*a*, *b*).

Stimulation of the hypothalamus by electrical pulses was shown by Harris and Woods (1958) to result in an increased thyroid activity in rabbits, that was maintained in the presence of a raised blood concentration of (radioactive) protein-bound iodine. In this much misquoted paper, Harris and Woods showed that electrical stimulation (by the remote control method) in the supraoptic region of the hypothalamus of *normal* conscious rabbits would result in an *increased function of the thyroid gland*, though stimulation in the region of the mid- and posterior-median eminence resulted in thyroid activation only after adrenalectomy. They ascribed these results to the fact that the TSH and adrenocorticotropic hormone (ACTH) fields of the hypothalamus overlap in the region of the median eminence and that simultaneous excitation of the adrenal cortex in some way blocks TSH secretion. These results were confirmed, in the main, in acute experiments in anaesthetized rabbits (Campbell, George and Harris, 1960) in which hypothalamic stimulation was applied by previously implanted electrodes and thyroid function assessed by measurements made on thyroid venous blood. Although these results using stimulation techniques could not be confirmed in rats in the laboratory of Dr. M. Greer, probably owing to difficulties in the stimulation technique used, D'Angelo and Snyder (1963) have recently reported that electrical stimulation of the anterior hypothalamus or the rostral portion of the median eminence in rats results in significant increases in the TSH concentration in the blood. There is very good agreement then between the results of experiments in which lesions have been made in the hypothalamus or electrical stimulation made in this part of the brain, that the area of the hypothalamus between the median eminence and optic chiasma, extending superiorly, is of importance in maintaining normal patterns of TSH secretion and thyroid function.

Stimulation of the hypothalamus by local cooling with observation of thyroid activity has been the subject of recent studies. It has long been known that the anterior hypothalamus is closely related to the mechanisms involved in maintaining a constant body temperature. It was logical to assume, then, that the neural mechanisms in the anterior hypothalamus concerned with temperature control acting by neural pathways (affecting respiration, vasodilatation, or sweating) would be integrated with those acting hormonally, namely on TSH secretion, which acts in turn on the thyroid gland to raise the general level of metabolism. Van Beugen and van der Werff ten Bosch (1961) had previously shown that removal of the forebrain anterior to the anterior commissure does not affect the thyroid activation that follows cold exposure. In important studies Andersson and co-workers (1962) found that local cooling of the anterior hypothalamic–preoptic region of the brain resulted in a marked rise of thyroid function. This effect of preoptic cooling will be dealt with in more detail in later papers.

There can be little doubt then that the anterior hypothalamus is directly concerned with regulating the resting basal level of TSH secretion and with mediating the increased secretion following environmental changes and reflex activation.

THE FEEDBACK ACTION OF CIRCULATING THYROID HORMONES

Aron, van Caulert and Stahl (1931) and Hoskins (1949) first developed and emphasized the view that the blood concentration of thyroxine plays an important rôle in regulating the rate of secretion of TSH. This feedback action of circulating thyroxine is today unquestioned, though it is likely that it is mainly related to setting the basal secretory rate of TSH, and that its action may be superseded by hypothalamic, reflex effects. For example, Harris and Woods (1958) found that electrical stimulation of the hypo-thalamus was effective in maintaining a sevenfold increase in thyroid activity in spite of a raised blood concentration of thyroxine.

The outstanding problem posed by this feedback effect of thyroxine at the present time is the central mechanism involved. Does the concentration of circulating thyroxine exert its action on thyrotropic secretion indirectly by an action at the hypothalamic level and so on anterior pituitary secretion, or by a direct action on the basophil thyrotropes of the anterior lobe? There is little doubt that gross changes in thyroxine concentration can affect anterior pituitary function directly.

(a) Thyroid activity is reduced by administration of thyroxine to animals with *isolated* pituitary glands, i.e. after effective stalk transection (Brown-Grant, Harris and Reichlin, 1957) or after pituitary transplantation (von Euler and Holmgren, 1956b). Hypophysectomized mice with intraocular transplants of the pituitary gland show thyroid stimulation when treated with thiouracil (Greer, 1952; Scow and Greer, 1953). Hemithyroidec-tomy also increases TSH secretion in hypophysectomized rats with intraocular transplants of the anterior pituitary gland (Khazin and Reichlin, 1961).

(b) Local infusions of thyroxine into the pituitary gland have been found to inhibit thyroid activity (von Euler and Holmgren, 1956a; Yamada and Greer, 1959; Harrison, 1961; Kendall, 1962).

(c) Minute transplants of thyroid tissue placed directly in the anterior pituitary gland prevent the development of characteristic thyroidectomy cells in their vicinity after removal of the thyroid gland (Bogdanove and Crabill, 1961).

There is little doubt then that anterior pituitary cells are them-selves sensitive to changes in concentration of the blood thyroxine. However this does not rule out the possibility that some region in the hypothalamus is also sensitive, perhaps more sensitive, to the blood level of thyroxine. The evidence here is equivocal. Von Euler and Holmgren (1956a) did not obtain any sign of thyroidal inhibition after local infusion of thyroxine into hypothalamic areas, although Yamada and Greer (1959) obtained a delayed thyroidal inhibition after thyroxine infusion into the anterior hypothalamus. Yamada (1959a, b) also found that intrahypo-thalamic infusion of thyroxine inhibited the development of propylthiouracil-induced goitres in rats. A criticism that has been levelled at these latter experiments is that the *delayed* responses may be explained by the diffusion of thyroxine (infused in rather large volumes, 0·02 ml.) to the pituitary gland, where the action was exerted.

In reviewing the feedback effects of the target gland hormones in general, it may be pointed out that in all probability (1) the osmotic pressure of the blood regulates posterior pituitary secretion of antidiuretic hormone through an action on the supraoptic nuclei of the hypothalamus, (2) the ovarian hormones exert their feedback effect via hypothalamic intermediation (Flerkó, 1963), and (3) cooling of the blood increases TSH secretion by hypo-thalamic intervention (it remains to be seen whether local cool-ing of the anterior pituitary gland results in increased TSH secretion). It is tempting to compare hypothalamic "centres" for regulating anterior pituitary secretion with medullary respiratory "centres" for regulating respiration. There seems little doubt that the respiratory centres of the medulla oblongata are sensitive not only to nervous reflex influences for the higher centres, but also to changes in carbon dioxide tension in the blood. Many years ago Dr. Seymour Reichlin suggested to me that the neuroendocrine axis might show a process of evolutionary development—similar to that of the central nervous system itself—in which the functions of the lower centres are taken over by the higher centres as they develop. Thus although the feedback effect of the target gland hormones in primitive forms may be exerted directly on the pituitary gland, with increasing development of the central ner-vous system, this feedback action may be taken over by the nervous system. In this connexion it may be pertinent to remark that carbon dioxide is present in the blood stream of vertebrates before the medullary respiratory centre is sensitive to its presence.

THE PRESENCE OF THYROID HORMONE AND THYROTROPIC HORMONE IN HYPOTHALAMIC AND NEUROHYPOPHYSIAL TISSUE

Although it was known some thirty years ago that the tuber cinereum had a relatively high iodine content, it was only with the introduction of isotopically labelled thyroxine that exact studies could be undertaken. Joliot and co-workers (1944; and see Courrier, 1952) showed that the pituitary of the rabbit accumulates radioactive thyroxine, and Courrier and co-workers (1951) and Jensen and Clark (1951) found that this concentration occurred in the posterior lobe. In the rabbit, monkey and dog (though not in some other species, such as the rat and guinea pig) the concentration of $[^{131}I]$thyroxine in the neurohypophysis may exceed that in the plasma; similar findings have been made using $[^{131}I]$tri-iodothyronine (Courrier et al., 1951; Courrier, 1952; Taurog et al., 1956; Ford and Gross, 1958a, b). Jensen and Clark (1951) and Taurog and co-workers (1956) observed that the median eminence also accumulated these isotopically labelled hormones, and Ford and Gross (1958a, b) demonstrated an uptake by the supraoptic and paraventricular nuclei of the hypothalamus. The uptake of the labelled hormones has been found to be increased in hypothyroid rats and rabbits, and decreased in hyperthyroid animals (Harper, Mattis and Boerne, 1952; Taurog et al., 1956; Ford, Kantounis and Lawrence, 1959; Ford, 1961). This latter phenomenon may be related to some extent to a dilution of the labelled hormone by unlabelled hormone in the plasma.

Although it is tempting to ascribe some aspects of the thyroxine feedback effects on TSH release to this affinity of hypophysial and diencephalic structures for thyroxine, there are various facts which militate against this view.

(a) The posterior or neural lobe of the pituitary has a high affinity for accumulating thyroid hormones in some forms but this gland is probably not functionally related to anterior pituitary activity. Although the posterior lobe is connected to the pars distalis (in animals such as the rat) by a few fine capillaries, these are so scanty in number as compared with the wealth of the vascular connexion to the pars distalis from the median eminence as to appear insignificant. Also in many forms the posterior pituitary is completely separated from the pars distalis by a connective tissue septum.

(b) The denervated (by pituitary stalk section) and atrophic posterior lobe of the rabbit still concentrates $[^{131}I]$thyroxine as does the normal lobe (Taurog et al., 1956).

(c) Taurog and co-workers (1956) found that the pineal gland in the rabbit also accumulates $[^{131}I]$thyroxine. They suggested that since the vessels of the pineal have a similar permeability to those of the posterior pituitary gland (cf. Wislocki and King, 1936) the accumulation of thyroid hormones by these glands may be related rather to their type of vascularization than to their function.

It may perhaps be mentioned in passing that the median eminence and pituitary gland may accumulate oestrogens and adrenal steroids (Courrier and Zizine, 1956; Michael, 1963) as well as thyroidal hormones.

Early studies indicated the presence of anterior pituitary hormones in the tuber cinereum. By implanting, or injecting extracts of, the tuber cinereum in immature animals Pighini (1935) and Weisschedel and Spatz (1942) claimed to have detected gonadotropic substances in this tissue. Schittenhelm and Eisler (1935) found that injection of a saline extract of the diencephalon of the cat resulted in thyroid hypertrophy and that similar extracts of other regions of the brain had no effect. In a more comprehensive study, Borell (1945) claimed to have detected thyrotropic hormone in extracts from the tuber cinereum and choroid plexus of brains of guinea pigs, rabbits, sheep and cattle, but not in similar extracts of the mammillary bodies or walls of the lateral ventricle. The tissues were treated with acetone and extracted with $0 \cdot 25$ per cent acetic acid; the assays were performed using the thyroid-cell height of the guinea pig. Borell found that the thyroid-stimulating substance in the tuber cinereum and choroid plexus was increased by previous exposure of the donor animal to cold and abolished by previous hypophysectomy. Heating the extracts of the tuber cinereum in a boiling water bath for one hour resulted in disappearance of the activity. It is difficult at the present time to assess the significance of these early results. Since it was not suspected that the tuber cinereum might contain substances responsible for releasing anterior pituitary hormones, tests do not seem to have been made on hypophysectomized animals. Thus these results could be explained in terms of the tuber cinereum containing TSH, or a factor capable of releasing TSH from the assay animal's own pituitary gland (thyrotropic releasing factor—TRF). With the recent arousal of interest in the possibility that extracts of the median eminence might have TRF activity, the fact that these extracts might also contain TSH has become an important consideration.

Recent evidence for the existence of TSH in hypothalamic tissue is given by Guillemin (1963) and in a later paper here (Reichlin, 1964). ACTH may also be present in the diencephalon

since its occurrence in the posterior pituitary gland (see Mialhe-
Voloss, 1958) and hypothalamus (see Guillemin, 1963) seems well
founded. Guillemin, Jutisz and Sakiz (1963) describe the presence
of a substance with the activity of luteinizing hormone (LH)
in extracts of the hypothalamus or median eminence of sheep.
There are at least indications then that the tuber cinereum contains
a higher content than other brain tissue of the thyroidal, ovarian
and adrenocortical hormones, TSH, LH and ACTH. If further
work confirms these findings, a most intriguing problem (concerning the significance of the presence of these hormones) will
await solution. It would be of much interest to know whether the
hormonal concentration in the tuber cinereum varies in different
physiological states in a manner similar to that reported by
Mialhe-Voloss (1958) for the ACTH content of the posterior
pituitary.

VASOPRESSIN AND THYROID FUNCTION

During recent experiments in my department it was observed
(Garcia, Harris and Schindler, 1964) that injection of dilute
acetic acid extracts of median eminence tissue increased thyroid
activity in the rabbit. Our interest at that time was to see whether
median eminence tissue contained a factor (TRF) with the property
of stimulating TSH release from the anterior pituitary gland.
These preliminary results were compatible with that view. Since
our median eminence extracts were in all probability contaminated
with vasopressin, and since many reports in the literature indicate
that vasopressin administration stimulates secretion of TSH, it was
decided to investigate the action of this posterior pituitary hormone
further.

In order to assess thyroid function, rabbits in which the thyroid
gland had been labelled with ^{131}I and in which endogenous TSH
secretion had been blocked with thyroxine, were used. On the
morning of the experiment a venous blood sample was with-
drawn, a 2-hr. intravenous infusion of the test substance was given,
hourly blood samples taken during and after the infusion, and the
radioactivity of the blood measured. Thyroidal activation was
detected by a rise in blood radioactivity during, and/or following
the infusion. At the end of the experiment the animal was killed,
the radioactivity in the thyroid measured and the rise in blood

radioactivity expressed as a percentage of stored hormone released from the thyroid gland. In summary, it was found that infusions of International Standard TSH gave a log dose: thyroid-response curve, linear over the range 10–1,000 m.-u. TSH. Infusions of vasopressin (highly purified lysine vasopressin; synthetic lysine and synthetic arginine vasopressin) at rates of 2·8–22 m-u./min. for 2 hr. led to an increased blood radioactivity similar in every respect to that seen following TSH. Chromatographic methods show that this rise in blood radioactivity was due largely to an increase in concentration of labelled thyroid hormone and partly to an increase in blood [131]I. To investigate the site of this action of vasopressin, the rabbits were divided into three groups—normal, hypophysectomized and sham-operated. Vasopressin infusions resulted in comparable increases in thyroid function in all these groups, including the hypophysectomized animals. Since vasopressin was found not to potentiate the action of TSH on the thyroid in the rabbit, and further experiments in collaboration with Dr. D. El Kabir showed no increase in plasma TSH during and after vasopressin infusions, the conclusion was drawn that vasopressin exerts, in some way, a direct stimulating effect on the thyroid gland of the rabbit.

A further investigation was then undertaken on the rat (Harris, Levine and Schindler, 1964). In outline, the experimental procedure in the rat was similar to that in the rabbit, but it was found that administration of vasopressin in the normal rat gave no sign of thyroidal activation (as observed by blood radioactivity measurements) although injection of 0·25–5·0 m-u. of TSH gave a detectable response. In animals which had been pretreated with oestrogens, however, vasopressin injections (i.v.) resulted in thyroidal activation.

From the above experiments there is no reason to suppose that vasopressin exerts a stimulating release on anterior pituitary TSH. Rather it seems that it can exert a direct stimulating action, in some way, on the thyroid gland. These results are reminiscent of those of Hilton and co-workers (1960), who found that vasopressin has a direct stimulating action on the adrenal cortex, and those of McCann and Taleisnik (1961) on the action of vasopressin on ovarian ascorbic acid.

Whatever the physiological significance (if any) of the action of vasopressin on the rabbit's thyroid gland, the above results do indicate that certain precautionary measures are necessary when extracts of median eminence tissue (very likely to contain vasopressin) are being investigated for their TRF activity.

NEUROHUMORAL CONTROL OF TSH SECRETION AND A THYROTROPIC–RELEASING FACTOR (TRF)

It is generally admitted that vascularization of the anterior pituitary gland by the hypophysial portal vessels is of basic importance in maintaining normal TSH secretion and a normal thyroid function. The mechanism involved, however, is not yet established. Two possibilities have received attention in the last few years.

(a) *Median eminence filtration hypothesis*. This hypothesis—first presented in detail by Brown-Grant (1957) and amplified by Purves (1960)—postulates that the median eminence extracts, or binds, thyroxine from the blood circulating in the primary plexus of the portal vessels, and that according to the amounts inactivated in this way the anterior pituitary is subjected to varying concentration of thyroid hormone in its blood supply. On this view the median eminence would, according to neural influences from the hypothalamus, extract more or less thyroxine and this would be reflected in increased or decreased secretion of TSH by the anterior pituitary. The main argument in support of this theory was the finding that the median eminence and posterior pituitary do in fact accumulate thyroxine (see discussion above). However this characteristic is species-variable, and is not limited to the median eminence. Further, one cannot extrapolate from these results and consider such a mechanism as a control mechanism for other pituitary hormones; it cannot explain, for example, the sudden release of luteinizing hormone which follows mating in the female rabbit, or the increased secretion of ACTH which follows stress in adrenalectomized animals. It would be of interest to see the effect of hypothalamic stimulation on the blood concentration of TSH in the thyroidectomized animal.

(b) *Neurohumoral theory*. It is probably true to say that most workers in the field provisionally accept the neurohumoral theory as being the most likely. This view postulates that nerve fibres from the hypothalamus enter the median eminence and terminate close to the primary capillary plexus of the portal

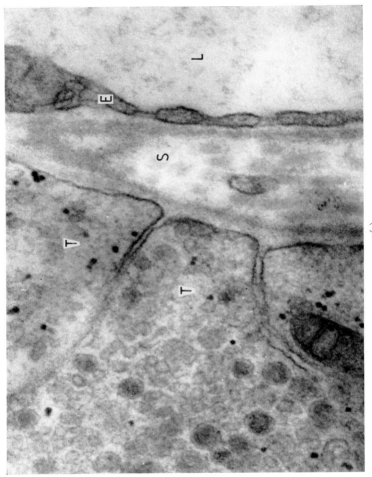

FIG. 1. Electron micro-
photographs of the median
eminence of the rat. Note
the lumen of the capillary
(L), the thin fenestrated
layer of capillary endo-
thelium (E), the peri-
vascular space (S) and the
nerve terminals (T) con-
taining synaptic vesicles as
small vacuolated ring-shape
structures. In (a) the nerve
terminals also contain more
solid-looking opaque
masses of neurosecretory
material. (a) × 91,500;
(b) × 45,000.

To face p. 12.

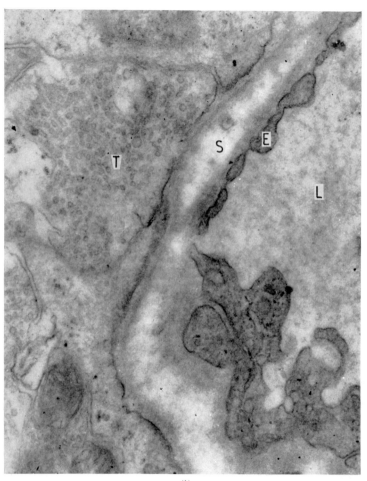

1 (b)

vessels. From these nerve terminals various transmitter agents (releasing factors, RF) are liberated into the vessels and carried to the anterior pituitary to control its secretory activity.

Recent studies of the median eminence with the electron microscope in the guinea pig (Barry and Cotte, 1960, 1961) and rat and rabbit (Bradbury and Harris, 1964) reveal a structure in conformity with these views. A very rich association between nerve terminals and capillaries is found, with the nerve terminals containing synaptic vesicles and neurosecretory material. The capillary endothelium, which is of the absorptive type, showing the presence of fenestrations, is immediately surrounded by a perivascular "space" which is continuous outwards with spaces which intervene between bundles of nerve terminals (see Fig. 1a and b). The structure is very similar to that of the posterior pituitary gland (neural lobe), and indicates that liberation of substances from the nerve terminals into the blood stream does in fact occur.

Attempts have been made in the last few years to extract a substance from median eminence tissue which is active in causing release of thyrotropic hormone from the anterior pituitary gland. It has been suggested that such a substance should be termed the thyrotropic-releasing factor (TRF). The many studies have been well and recently reviewed in detail by D'Angelo (1963) and Guillemin (1963). Perhaps the most promising approach at the moment is that of Guillemin and his collaborators (1962; and see Guillemin, 1963) in which acid extracts were made of the hypothalamus of sheep and purified by fractionation on Sephadex. The TRF fraction so obtained lost its activity after enzymic hydrolysis, was thermostable, and was not active in increasing thyroid activity in hypophysectomized animals under conditions in which TSH was as active as in normal animals. The TRF fraction, on administration to normal animals, excited the release of TSH and gave a response which was linearly related to the logarithm of the dose injected. The TRF fraction was found to lose its activity if injected into animals pretreated with thyroxine.

Future studies will no doubt be concerned with identification of the chemical structure of releasing factors. There are strong indications that the releasing factors (CRF, LRF) are polypeptides with a slightly higher molecular weight than oxytocin and vasopressin (see Symposium on Polypeptides, 1964). However before the neurohumoral theory can be said to be fully established it will be necessary to show that these compounds are present in hypophysial portal vessel blood in amounts which vary with the rate of secretion of the various anterior pituitary hormones.

REFERENCES

ALLEN, B. M. (1916). *Science*, **44,** 755.

ANDERSSON, B., EKMAN, L., GALE, C. C., and SUNDSTEN, J. W. (1962). *Life Sciences*, **1,** 1.

ARON, M., CAULERT, C. VAN and STAHL, J. (1931). *C.R. Soc. Biol. (Paris)*, **107,** 64.

BARRY, J., and COTTE, G. (1960). *C.R. Soc. Biol. (Paris)*, **154,** 2054.

BARRY, J., and COTTE, G. (1961). *Z. Zellforsch.*, **53,** 714.

BEUGEN, L. VAN, and WERFF TEN BOSCH, J. J. VAN DER (1961). *Acta endocr. (Kbh.)*, **37,** 470.

BOGDANOVE, E. M., and CRABILL, E. V. (1961). *Endocrinology*, **69,** 581.

BOGDANOVE, E. M., and HALMI, N. S. (1953). *Endocrinology*, **53,** 274.

BOGDANOVE, E. M., SPIRTOS, B. N., and HALMI, N. S. (1955). *Endocrinology*, **57,** 302.

BORELL, U. (1945). On the transport route of the thyrotropic hormone, the occurrence of the latter in different parts of the brain and its effect on the thyroidea. Stockholm: Haeggströms.

BRADBURY, S., and HARRIS, G. W. (1964). Unpublished.

BROLIN, S. E. (1945). *Acta anat. (Basel)*, **2,** suppl. 3.

BROLIN, S. E. (1947). *Acta physiol. scand.*, **14,** 233.

BROWN-GRANT, K. (1957). *Ciba Found. Coll. Endocr.*, **10,** 97. London: Churchill.

BROWN-GRANT, K. (1964). *In* The Pituitary Gland, vol. 2, ch. 7. London: Butterworth. In press.

BROWN-GRANT, K., HARRIS, G. W., and REICHLIN, S. (1957). *J. Physiol. (Lond.)*, **136,** 364.

CAHANE, M., and CAHANE, T. (1936). *Rev. franç. Endocr.*, **14,** 472.

CAHANE, M., and CAHANE, T. (1938). *Acta med. scand.*, **94,** 320.

CAMPBELL, H. J., GEORGE, R., and HARRIS, G. W. (1960). *J. Physiol. (Lond.)*, **152,** 527.

COURRIER, R. (1952). *Ciba Found. Coll. Endocr.*, **4,** 311. London: Churchill.

COURRIER, R., HOREAU, A., MAROIS, M., and MOREL, F. (1951). *C.R. Acad. Sci. (Paris)*, **232,** 1009.

COURRIER, R., and ZIZINE, L. (1956). *C.R. Acad. Sci. (Paris)*, **242,** 315.

D'ANGELO, S. A. (1958). *J. Endocr.*, **17,** 286.

D'ANGELO, S. A. (1963). *In* Advances in Neuroendocrinology, Ch. 6. Urbana: University of Illinois Press.

D'ANGELO, S. A., and SNYDER, J. (1963). *Endocrinology*, **73,** 75.

D'ANGELO, S. A., and TRAUM, R. E. (1956). *Endocrinology*, **59,** 593.

D'ANGELO, S. A., and TRAUM, R. E. (1958). *Ann. N.Y. Acad. Sci.*, **72,** 239.

DONOVAN, B. T. and HARRIS, G. W. (1956). *J. Physiol. (Lond.)*, **131,** 102.

EULER, C. VON, and HOLMGREN, B. (1956a). *J. Physiol. (Lond.)*, **131,** 125.

EULER, C. VON, and HOLMGREN, B. (1956b). *J. Physiol. (Lond.)*, **131,** 137.

FLERKÓ, B. (1963). *In* Advances in Neuroendocrinology, Ch. 7. Urbana: University of Illinois Press.

FLORSHEIM, W. H. (1958). *Endocrinology*, **62**, 783.

FORD, D. H. (1961). *Gen. comp. Endocr.*, **1**, 59.

FORD, D. H., and GROSS, J. (1958a). *Endocrinology*, **62**, 416.

FORD, D. H., and GROSS, J. (1958b). *Endocrinology*, **63**, 549.

FORD, D. H., KANTOUNIS, S., and LAWRENCE, R. (1959). *Endocrinology*, **64**, 972.

GANONG, W. F., FREDRICKSON, D. S., and HUME, D. M. (1955). *Endocrinology*, **57**, 355.

GARCIA, J., HARRIS, G. W., and SCHINDLER, W. J. (1964). *J. Physiol. (Lond.)*, **170**, 487.

GOLDBERG, R. C., and KNOBIL, E. (1957). *Endocrinology*, **61**, 742.

GREER, M. A. (1951). *Proc. Soc. exp. Biol. (N.Y.)*, **77**, 603.

GREER, M. A. (1952). *J. clin. Endocr.*, **12**, 1259.

GREER, M. A., and ERWIN, H. L. (1954). *J. clin. Invest.*, **33**, 938.

GREER, M. A., SCOW, R. O., and GROBSTEIN, C. (1953). *Proc. Soc. exp. Biol. (N.Y.)*, **82**, 28.

GUILLEMIN, R. (1963). *J. Physiol. (Paris)*, **55**, 7.

GUILLEMIN, R., JUTISZ, M., and SAKIZ, E. (1963). *C.R. Acad. Sci. (Paris)*, **256**, 504.

GUILLEMIN, R., YAMAZAKI, E., JUTISZ, M., and SAKIZ, E. (1962). *C.R. Acad. Sci. (Paris)*, **255**, 1018.

HARPER, E. O., MATTIS, P. A., and BOERNE, J. W. (1952). *Fed. Proc.*, **11**, 355.

HARRIS, G. W., and JACOBSOHN, D. (1952). *Proc. roy. Soc. B*, **139**, 263.

HARRIS, G. W., LEVINE, S., and SCHINDLER, W. J. (1964). *J. Physiol. (Lond.)*, **170**, 516.

HARRIS, G. W., and WOODS, J. W. (1958). *J. Physiol. (Lond.)*, **143**, 246.

HARRISON, T. S. (1961). *Endocrinology*, **68**, 466.

HILTON, J. G., SCIAN, L. F., WESTERMANN, D. C., NAKANO, J., and KRUESI, O. R. (1960). *Endocrinology*, **67**, 298.

HOSKINS, R. G. (1949). *J. clin. Endocr.*, **9**, 1429.

JENSEN, J. M., and CLARK, D. E. (1951). *J. Lab. clin. Med.*, **38**, 663.

JOLIOT, F., COURRIER, R., HOREAU, A., and SUE, P. (1944). *C.R. Soc. Biol. (Paris)*, **138**, 325.

KENDALL, W. J. (1962). *Endocrinology*, **71**, 452.

KHAZIN, A., and REICHLIN, S. (1961). *Endocrinology*, **68**, 914.

KNIGGE, K. M. (1961). *Endocrinology*, **68**, 101.

KNIGGE, K. M., and BIERMAN, S. M. (1958). *Amer. J. Physiol.*, **192**, 625.

LOEB, L., and BASSETT, R. B. (1929). *Proc. Soc. exp. Biol. (N.Y.)*, **27**, 490.

MARTINI, L., DE POLI, A., PECILE, A., SAITO, S., and TANI, F. (1959). *J. Endocr.*, **19**, 164.

McCANN, S. M., and TALEISNIK, S. (1961). *Endocrinology*, **68**, 1071.

MIALHE-VOLOSS, C. (1958). *Acta endocr. (Kbh.)*, **28**, suppl. 35.

MICHAEL, R. P. (1964). *In* Hormonal Steroids, vol. 2, ed. Martini, L. New York: Academic Press, in press.

NIKITOVITCH-WINER, M., and EVERETT, J. W. (1958). *Endocrinology*, **63**, 916.

NIKITOVITCH-WINER, M., and EVERETT, J. W. (1959). *Endocrinology*, **65**, 357.

OLIVECRONA, H. (1957). *Acta physiol. scand.*, **40**, suppl. 136.

PIGHINI, G. (1935). *Endocrinology*, **19,** 293.

PURVES, H. D. (1960). First International Congress of Endocrinology, Copenhagen, July 1960. Abstracts of symposium lectures, p. 21.

REICHLIN, S. (1960a). *Endocrinology*, **66,** 327.

REICHLIN, S. (1960b). *Endocrinology*, **66,** 340.

REICHLIN, S. (1964). This volume, p. 17.

SCHITTENHELM, A., and EISLER, B. (1935). *Z. ges. exp. Med.*, **95,** 121.

SCOW, R. O., and GREER, M. A. (1953). *J. clin. Endocr.*, **13,** 855.

SCOW, R. O., and GREER, M. A. (1955). *Endocrinology*, **56,** 590.

SMITH, P. E. (1916). *Anat. Rec.*, **11,** 57.

SMITH, P. E. (1927). *J. Amer. med. Ass.*, **88,** 158.

Symposium on Polypeptides (1964). Kalamazoo: Upjohn Co., in press.

TAUROG, A., HARRIS, G. W., TONG, W., and CHAIKOFF, I. L. (1956). *Endocrinology*, **59,** 34.

UOTILA, U. U. (1939). *Endocrinology*, **25,** 605.

UOTILA, U. U. (1940). *Res. Publ. Ass. nerv. ment. Dis.*, **20,** 580.

WEISSCHEDEL, E., and SPATZ, H. (1942). *Dtsch. med. Wschr.*, **68,** 1221.

WISLOCKI, G. B., and KING, L. S. (1936). *Amer. J. Anat.*, **58,** 421.

YAMADA, T. (1959a). *Endocrinology*, **65,** 216.

YAMADA, T. (1959b). *Endocrinology*, **65,** 920.

YAMADA, T., and GREER, M. A. (1959). *Endocrinology*, **64,** 559.

FUNCTION OF THE HYPOTHALAMUS IN REGULATION OF PITUITARY-THYROID ACTIVITY*

SEYMOUR REICHLIN

Endocrine Unit, Department of Medicine,
University of Rochester School of Medicine and Dentistry,
Rochester, New York

As reviewed in previous publications (Brown-Grant, 1960; Bogdanove, 1962; Reichlin, 1963a) and most recently by Professor Harris in his introductory remarks to this conference, experimental evidence that the thyrotropic function of the pituitary is subject both to feedback control by the thyroid hormones and to neural control by the hypothalamus is extensive and widely accepted. Still subject to investigation and debate are the mode of interaction between the neural and humoral controlling factors by which the TSH secretory process is regulated in conformity with the physiological requirements of the animal, and the intimate molecular details of mechanisms underlying both neural and feedback regulation of the pituitary thyrotrope cell. Experiments to be presented in this paper deal with two aspects of these problems. The first concerns the nature of the stimulus to which the hypothalamus is sensitive in its regulation of thyroid function; the second summarizes the efforts of this laboratory to identify a hypothalamic thyrotropin-releasing factor (TRF) whose existence was predicted by the portal-vessel chemotransmitter hypothesis, and whose isolation has been claimed by a number of workers including Shibusawa, Nishi and Abe (1959), by Schreiber and co-workers (1963), and by Guillemin and co-workers (1963).

CENTRAL THERMOCEPTIVE CONTROL OF THYROID FUNCTION

The most economical explanation of the mode of interaction between neural and hormonal regulatory systems is that the portion of the brain concerned with thyrotropic hormone control

* Studies reported here were supported by U.S. Public Health Service Grant No. NB 04051, and were carried out in collaboration with Dr. James N. McClure, Miss Rita L. Boshans, Miss Martha Labombard and Mr. Larry Kaplan.

is the site of feedback action by thyroid hormone. This hypothesis was tested in rabbits by Brown-Grant, Harris and Reichlin (1957); stalk section failed to interfere with the usual inhibitory effects of thyroxine on the pituitary-thyroid axis. From work with pituitary transplants in rabbits (von Euler and Holmgren, 1956a) and rats (cf. Khazin and Reichlin, 1961; Reichlin, 1963b), it appears that the pituitary is autonomously responsive to changes in thyroxine concentration over a wide range from low to high values. Von Euler and his collaborators have in two separate investigations failed to demonstrate that the hypothalamus is locally sensitive to thyroxine (in the rabbit) (von Euler and Holmgren, 1956b; Harrison, 1961), while Yamada and Greer (1959), although they have produced thyroid inhibition by direct intrahypothalamic injections of thyroxine (in the rat), concede that the effects observed follow a different time course from that which follows either systemic or intrapituitary administration. These observations have raised serious doubts that a thyroxine-sensitive "receptor" in the hypothalamus or a hypothalamic-pituitary connexion are essential links in feedback control of the pituitary-thyroid axis.

An alternative explanation of the nature of the stimulus to which the hypothalamus is sensitive in its regulation of TSH secretion was suggested by an analysis of the topographical localization of body-temperature-controlling and thyroid-controlling regions in the brain of the rat. As might have been anticipated from classical studies of temperature regulation in a variety of animal species with localized brain damage (Ström, 1960) and the "thyrotropic" area localization studies by Greer (1957), lesions affecting body temperature control were found to be located close to those affecting thyroid function (Reichlin, 1960) (Fig. 1).

Since thermoregulatory reflexes are responsive to thermosensitive neurones in the preoptic area, it seemed reasonable to postulate that the hypothalamic component of pituitary-thyroid regulation was also controlled by local temperature rather than by local thyroxine concentration. Through this temperature-sensing system, thyroid function might be integrated with autonomic and behavioural components of caloric homoeostasis. Dr. Andersson and his collaborators (1963a, b) independently put forth the same suggestion, and have published several experiments supporting this viewpoint.

To test this hypothesis, Dr. James McClure and I (1964) determined in rats the effects of localized hypothalamic and preoptic area cooling on body temperature and thyroid function. In the first series of experiments, local cooling was accomplished by use of a double-lumened, 20 gauge, stainless steel tube, introduced

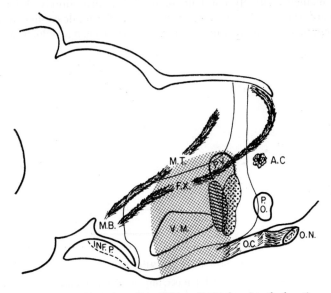

FIG. 1. Semi-schematic outline of the rat brain showing the location of lesions which produced hyperthermia (stippled), and those which produced inhibition of thyroidal ^{131}I release rate (hatched). The larger shaded area indicates the location of lesions (from studies of Greer, 1957) which inhibit thyroid response to goitrogen administration. The close topographical association of temperature-controlling and thyroid-controlling response is demonstrated. (From Reichlin, S. [1960]. *Endocrinology*, **66**, 340.)

into various regions of the brain under stereotaxic control, and maintained in position for chronic experiments with stainless steel screws and dental acrylic cement. Ether was led into the tip of the needle through concentric 27 gauge hypodermic tubing, and negative pressure was applied to the side arm of the outer needle to cause evaporative cooling (Fig. 2). Temperatures 3 to 5°C below normal brain temperature were produced by this device.

Rectal temperature was measured with a thermistor thermometer. During the control and cooling periods the animals were confined to a relatively small acrylic plastic cage to permit adequate observations and continuous cooling.

During baseline control observations, rectal temperature remained relatively constant, or tended to drift slowly downwards (Fig. 3). Less than one minute after thermode cooling was begun, rectal temperature began to rise, a change which was

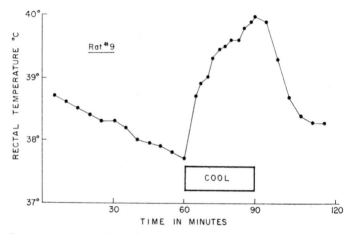

FIG. 3. Response of rectal temperature in the restrained rat to one half-hour period of preoptic area cooling.

almost always accompanied by visible shivering movements. Immediately upon cessation of cooling, body temperature began to fall. These effects could be elicited over prolonged periods: continued cooling for seven hours in one experiment induced continued fever for the entire time. A number of placements were studied. Those giving hyperthermic responses were localized to the classical preoptic area, and also impinged upon the "thyrotropic" area (Fig. 4). Because the thermodes are so large, relative to brain size, and the zone of cooling not clearly defined, localizations must be taken as being only approximations.

Thyroidal ^{131}I release curves (Reichlin, 1957) were determined in seven animals subjected to cooling or sham cooling for seven to eight hours. Thyroid acceleration was not observed in any of

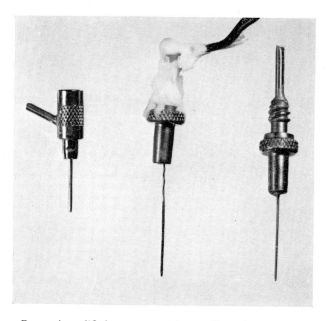

Fig. 2. A modified 20 gauge, stainless steel hypodermic needle served as a thermode for evaporative cooling. The unit on the left was sealed at the tip and embedded in the brain under stereotaxic control. When cooling was to be carried out the inner, 27 gauge needle (on the right), was inserted, thus sealing the top of the thermode. A vacuum was applied to the side arm and a source of ether connected to the central tube. The centre insert was a fine Nichrome wire-wound core which served as a local heating device. Results of heating studies are not reported in the paper.

To face p. 20.

the five cooled animals. In fact, in each animal, there was a prompt inhibition of thyroidal ^{131}I release, persisting for approximately 12 hours after cessation of the cooling period. The release curves were painfully reminiscent of the thyroid inhibitory response to restraint in the rabbit as reported by Brown-Grant and co-workers (1954a) and of the response to excessive cold exposure in the rat

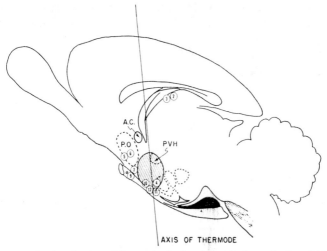

AXIS OF THERMODE

FIG. 4. The distribution of thermode tip placements in the rat brain, which, when cooled, produced fever or no effect. Positive placements are: 4, 5, 6, 7, 9, 10, 11, 12. Negative placements are: 2 and 3; placements in other animals in temporal lobe (not plotted). The axis of the thermode is shown because cooling occurred in a parallel line from the tip upwards along the course of the thermode.

(Brown-Grant, 1956). Sham cooling produced similar inhibitory effects.

It was concluded that the observed changes in thyroid function were due to stressful restraint. The restraint did not interfere with body temperature response, but might have masked changes in thyroid function.

Evaporative cooling proved difficult to use in unrestrained animals. Another procedure was then developed which depended upon conductive cooling through a metal rod (copper or gold), connected to a metal capsule attached to the skull, through which cool water at a temperature between 21 and 26° c was circulated. Conductive cooling devices were placed in a total of 27 rats. After a period of one to three weeks, thyroidal ^{131}I release rate was determined beginning 24 hours after the injection of [131]I. Neck counts were made at short intervals, particularly during the ten-hour cooling period. Sixteen of the 27 animals remained healthy throughout this period and gave release curves with minimal scatter and suitable for analysis by the method of least squares. Of the 16, 13 animals displayed thyroid acceleration during the

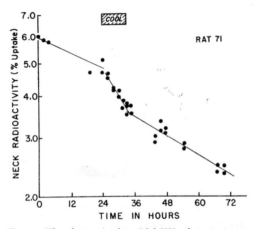

FIG. 5. The change in thyroidal ^{131}I release rate produced by local hypothalamic cooling. Unlike the previous experiments, the animal was not restrained and cooling was accomplished by conduction.

cooling period (Fig. 5), two had thyroid inhibition and the thyroid release rate was unchanged in the remaining one. For the entire group, mean release rate (in per cent per hour) before cooling was $1\cdot07\pm0\cdot11$ (s.e.); during cooling, $1\cdot92\pm0\cdot26$; and after cooling, $0\cdot92\pm0\cdot07$. Difference between baseline and cooling periods was statistically significant ($P<0\cdot001$). Body temperature response to local cooling was determined in most of these animals during subsequent one-hour periods of local cooling. Nine animals that had displayed thyroid acceleration upon cooling also manifested fever upon cooling. The remaining animals had dissociated febrile and thyroid acceleration responses in various combinations. Placements of thermodes which caused thyroid acceleration lay between the supraoptic area and the anterior commissure, and in one animal in the posterior hypothalamus. Several placements in the region of the anterior commissure were also without effect on thyroid function (Fig. 6).

From these observations, the conclusion was drawn that the anterior hypothalamic region in addition to being thermosensitive for the regulation of body temperature is thermosensitive

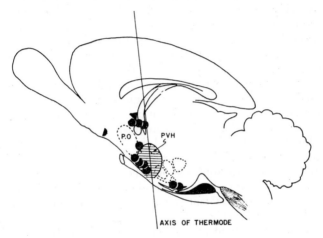

FIG. 6. Plotted on a diagram of a sagittal section through the rat brain are tip placements of thermodes, cooling of which induced an increase in thyroidal ^{131}I release (black circles). The triangle placement produced no effect, and the half circle, inhibition.

for the control of thyroid function. These responses are elicited from similar, perhaps identical regions, and restraint appears to inhibit the thyroid effects without affecting febrile response. These results confirm the work of Andersson and his co-workers (1963a, b) in the goat, published while our own studies were being done, and lend further support to the view that the hypothalamic component of pituitary-thyroid regulation is involved in caloric homoeostasis.

Although it seems most reasonable to conclude that a direct thermal stimulus can trigger an immediate change in TSH secretion, the possibility that the response is secondary to peripheral metabolic activity, i.e. shivering and increased thyroxine degradation, cannot be excluded without specific studies.

THYROID–STIMULATING ACTIVITY OF BOVINE STALK-MEDIAN EMINENCE TISSUE

Accumulating evidence that the secretion of thyrotropic hormone is under the influence of the nervous system, and the reasonably certain identification of corticotropin-releasing factor (CRF) and luteinizing-hormone-releasing factor (LRF) in hypothalamic extracts, have spurred on the search by many workers for neurohumoral substances capable of influencing the synthesis and release of TSH. In previous work from this laboratory, the hypothalamic polypeptides, vasopressin and oxytocin have been found to be without effect on the pituitary-thyroid system of the rat (Reichlin, 1957; Crosson, Falch and Reichlin, 1960). Although vasopressin does have thyroid-stimulating action in the rabbit (Schindler and Harris, 1963) and the dog (Lipscomb, Hathway and Gard, 1961) this is due to a direct action independent of the pituitary. Repeated studies in our laboratory failed to reveal any effects of even large doses of pitressin on thyroid function in the mouse, and Brown-Grant (1960) has obtained similar negative results in the guinea pig.

Further efforts to identify a "TRF" led to the study of thyroid-stimulating properties of extracts of hypothalamus of the ox. Ox tissues were used because they are the largest and most convenient commercial source of hypothalamic tissue. The region taken for assay was limited to the pituitary stalk and median eminence (SME). For most studies homogenates were made in physiological saline solution, and the supernatants utilized for assay after centrifugation. In later studies, following the reports of Porath and Schally (1962) and of Guillemin and his co-workers (1962), median eminence extracts in 2N-acetic acid were separated by gel filtration on Sephadex G-25. Assay for thyroid-stimulating effects in mice was carried out according to the method of McKenzie (1958) with some variations. The major modifications were that the animals were fed on a low iodine test diet (Nutritional Biochemical Corp., Cleveland, Ohio), and distilled water *ad libitum*. Blood samples for radioactivity counts were taken from

6/6/ 44   C482

the cavernous sinus through the orbit directly into 100 µl. constriction pipettes. For most studies, mice were given thyroxine as in the original McKenzie method. In some experiments, thyroxine was not given, and in others, hypophysectomized mice were used. Test materials were injected into the tail veins in a volume of 0·5 ml. and blood samples were taken before and two hours after injection. Radioactivity of samples was determined

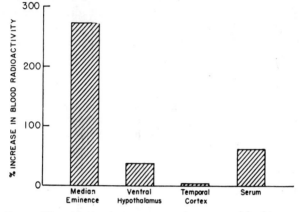

FIG. 7. Thyroid stimulatory response (as measured by bioassay in [^{131}I]thyroxine-pretreated mice) to extracts of various regions of bovine brain (50 mg. tissue). Stalk–median tissue gave greatest responses, ventral hypothalamus (less SME) smaller responses, and cortex was without activity.

using a well scintillation counter. Results in most experiments are expressed as percentage change of the two-hour specimen as compared with initial values. In certain experiments, a more meaningful evaluation of the results was given by consideration of the magnitude rather than the percentage change of blood radioactivity.

Extracts of SME produced significant changes in blood radioactivity in the [^{131}I]thyroxine-pretreated mouse (Fig. 7). Extracts of similar quantities of ventral hypothalamus, excluding the median eminence, had less marked effects; extracts of temporal cortex exerted no thyroid-stimulating effect. The response to median eminence was not due to contamination with peripheral blood since 50 µl. of bovine serum, which corresponds to twice

2

the amount of serum contained in the median eminence fraction, gave a significant stimulating effect, but much less than that found after SME injection.

These data indicated that a thyroid-stimulating material was present in median eminence tissue. Current views about chemical thyroid stimulators suggest that four types of substance might be responsible for the effects observed. The material might be TSH, "TRF", a late-acting thyroid stimulator (LATS) (McKenzie, 1961), or an agent like vasopressin, MSH, or adrenaline which in some species is reported to exert direct effects on the thyroid independent of the pituitary. Studies designed to identify the thyroid-stimulating material are outlined in Table I. Space does

TABLE I

COMPARISON OF THE THYROID-STIMULATING PROPERTIES OF UNFRAC-
TIONATED BOVINE STALK-MEDIAN EMINENCE EXTRACTS (SME) WITH THOSE
OF AUTHENTIC BEEF TSH (NIH)

	SME	TSH
Short duration of action (2 hr. peak)	+	+
Inactivated at 100° C	+	+
Inactivated by Na periodate	+	+
Inactivated by anti-TSH antibody	+	+
Active in hypophysectomized mice	+	+

not permit detailed presentation of the data, which have appeared in abstract form (Reichlin and Boshans, 1963).

The brief duration of action excluded the possibility that the material is LATS. In its rapid inactivation by boiling and periodate oxidation, the material also closely resembles TSH. SME extract was inactivated by incubation with rabbit antibody formed against ox TSH. This latter finding cannot be used to prove absolute identity of the material with authentic TSH, however, since the activity of endogenous mouse TSH is also blocked by the anti-body. It can be concluded from the antibody work, however, that the material is either TSH or TRF, but that it cannot be operating independently of a TSH component. Such materials as vasopressin, adrenaline, or MSH are thus excluded. The most convincing evidence that the activity of unfractionated SME tissue was due to TSH was the demonstration of equal potency in hypophysectomized animals and in thyroxine-treated intact mice.

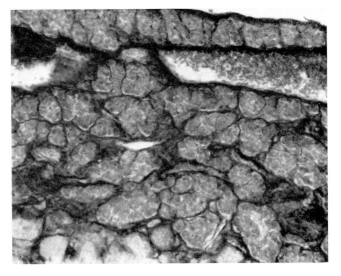

FIG. 8. Microphotograph of cells of the pars tuberalis of the ox to show its glandular appearance, and the stainable material within follicular epithelial formations. (× 165.)

To face p. 27.

The source of TSH within the SME was of considerable interest as it might be present merely as the result of reflux from anterior pituitary sinusoids, it might be concentrated from the circulating blood in the same way as thyroxine (Ford and Gross, 1958), trypan blue (Wislocki and King, 1936), or growth hormone (Salmon *et al.*, 1962) are concentrated in neurohypophysial tissue, it might be (as was suggested many years ago by Borrell, 1945) the usual pathway of secretion of TSH, or, finally, it might actually arise in secretory cells of this region.

Microscopic examination of SME tissue (Fig. 8) reveals a surprisingly large amount of glandular tissue of the pars tuberalis, initially emphasized by Atwell (1938). The cells of the pars tuberalis are arranged in cords and follicles. Within the cells, which are relatively pale-staining as contrasted with the remainder of the anterior pituitary, very small granules are found which take the periodic-acid Schiff (PAS) stain. Within the lumens of some of the follicles, PAS-staining material can be found. More specific methods will be required to prove that these granules contain TSH, but it seems quite possible that pars tuberalis cells do secrete this hormone and probably other pituitary hormones such as ACTH and LH which have been demonstrated in extracts of this region.

Although the study of unfractionated median eminence extracts gave evidence that TSH was the only thyroid-stimulating substance present in this tissue, the possibility was considered that large amounts of TSH present in this tissue might be masking much smaller quantities of a TRF material. The reasonableness of this hypothesis was further supported by the published studies of Guillemin and collaborators (1962) who stated that thyroid-stimulating material was present both in a large molecular weight fraction and in a small molecular weight polypeptide fraction of sheep median eminence tissue.

Beef SME extract was then subjected to Sephadex G-25 separation on a preparative scale (Fig. 9). When this was tested in thyroxine-treated mice, all of the thyroid-stimulating activity was found to reside in the large molecular weight fraction. It was concluded that all of the thyroid-stimulating activity of SME tissue which is demonstrable in the standard McKenzie assay (thyroxine-treated mouse) is attributable to TSH.

Since any effect of a TRF might be blocked or altered by

thyroxine treatment (a possibility also suggested by Guillemin), the thyroid-stimulating effects of various hypothalamic fractions were then tested in mice, which, unlike the standard McKenzie preparation, were not treated with thyroxine. These animals are

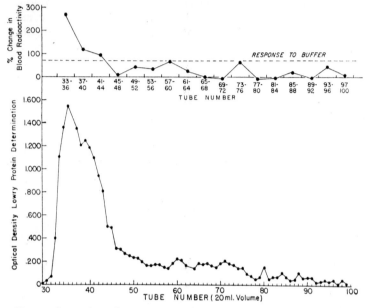

FIG. 9. Separation of SME extracts on Sephadex G-25. Extraction was carried out with 2N-acetic acid, and the supernatant placed on the column. Pyridine acetate, 0·1 M, pH 5, was used to elute the column. Abscissa: successive 20 ml. collections; ordinate: protein content measured by method of Lowry *et al.* (1951). Above the protein separation is shown the response to injection of 0·5 ml. of eluate from different portions of the separated extract in [131I]thyroxine-pretreated mice. All of the TSH activity appeared to be restricted to the large molecular weight fraction.

relatively insensitive to TSH, but 5 to 10 per cent of the amount of TSH contained in a mouse pituitary will give significant thyroid-stimulating effects in these animals, indicating that the release of this fraction of stored TSH can be detected. A total of 317 mg. of small molecular weight fractions was obtained from 600 SME units (wet weight, 42 g.). In amounts up to 3 mg. no effect of these materials on 131I release in thyroxine-treated mice was observed, indicating their freedom from TSH. Blood radio-activity decreases with time in normal animals. A stimulating effect on thyroid function may therefore be manifested not only by a rise in radioactivity concentration, but by a decrease less than that observed in control animals. Three mg. of small molecular weight fractions did in fact affect blood radioactivity (Table II).

TABLE II

RESPONSE OF BLOOD RADIOACTIVITY IN NORMAL ^{131}I-TREATED ANIMALS TO THE INJECTION OF SMALL MOLECULAR WEIGHT FRACTIONS FROM MEDIAN EMINENCE EXTRACTS (2 HR. RESPONSE)

	Treatment	No. of animals	Response Change %	S.E. ±
A	Saline control	6	− 27	5
B	Small molecular fraction	8	− 4	3
C	TSH (4 m-u.)	10	+ 10	8
	Statistical comparison		A vs. B $P < 0.001$	
			A vs. C $P < 0.01$	

According to Yamazaki, Sakiz and Guillemin (1963), partial thyroxination of test animals heightens the sensitivity of the assay to TRF. These workers used young rats instead of mice. Partially thyroxinized mice (a single injection of 5 μg. thyroxine at the beginning of assay set-up) were therefore tested with the small molecular weight fraction. Significant thyroid stimulation was observed in these animals (Table III).

TABLE III

BLOOD RADIOACTIVITY CHANGE IN PARTIALLY THYROXINIZED MICE TO FRACTIONS OF MEDIAN EMINENCE EXTRACT (2 hr. response)

Treatment	No. of animals	Response %	S.E.
Saline control	6	− 19	7
TSH (2 m-u.)	8	103	30
Small molecular fraction	11	68	22
Statistical comparison:			
Small molecular fraction vs. saline,		$P < 0.02$	

DISCUSSION

In this paper evidence has been presented that the hypothalamus participates in thyrotropic hormone regulation in two quite different ways. The preoptic-anterior hypothalamic area appears

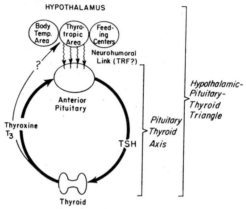

FIG. 10. Schema of the hypothalamic-pituitary-thyroid relationship. The major feedback control is illustrated as occurring between the pituitary and the thyroid gland. A smaller arrow (with a question mark) indicates that feedback control may also be exerted at the hypothalamic level. It is postulated that the anterior lobe thyrotrope cell is subject to two main interacting chemical influences. The first, TRF, a neurohormone found in hypophysial-portal blood, stimulates, and the second, thyroid hormone, inhibits, TSH secretion. Concentration of TRF depends upon neural factors which are in turn linked to the maintenance of caloric homoeostasis, while thyroxine concentration depends upon the rate of thyroxine synthesis, release and degradation in the periphery.

to be sensitive to temperature change; cooling of this region induces fever and activates the thyroid gland. Lesions in the same general area also affect body temperature regulation and bring about inhibition of pituitary-thyroid activity. The median eminence portion of the hypothalamus, that specialized region in which the primary plexus of the hypophysial portal circulation ramifies, has been found to contain, in addition to TSH which may arise from pars tuberalis epithelial cells, minute amounts of a small molecular weight substance which is not TSH, but which is capable of stimulating thyroid function in normal animals, although not in those treated with large amounts of thyroxine. This material is probably thyrotropin-releasing factor.

These observations, together with the well-demonstrated fact that the pituitary is autonomously reactive to local thyroxine concentration over a wide range of values, fit in well with a schema recently proposed (Reichlin, 1963a, b) (Fig. 10). According to this view, the principal feedback regulation by thyroid hormone is directly upon the pituitary gland, but the set-point of the system is established via hypothalamic drive, which is in turn sensitive to body temperature and linked to caloric homoeostasis. The thyrotrope cell thus appears to be dominated by two interacting chemical stimuli: one, TRF, which stimulates, the other, thyroid hormone, which inhibits, TSH secretion. Excess thyroxine inhibits the response to the neural drive, as occurred in these experiments, and in those reported by Guillemin and co-workers (1962, 1963) and by Andersson and co-workers (1963a). Normal blood levels of thyroxine do not interfere with increased neurohumoral drive in hypothalamic cooling, following electrical stimulation or after the injection of exogenous thyrotropin-releasing factor.

REFERENCES

ANDERSSON, B., EKMAN, L., GALE, C. C., and SUNDSTEN, J. W. (1963a). *Acta physiol. scand.*, **59**, 12.

ANDERSSON, B., GALE, C. C., and OHGA, A. (1963b). *Acta physiol. scand.*, **59**, 67.

ATWELL, W. J. (1938). *Ass. Res. nerv. Dis. Proc.*, **17**, 377.

BOGDANOVE, E. M. (1962). *Fed. Proc.*, **21**, 623.

BORRELL, U. (1945). *Acta med. scand.*, Suppl., **161**, 1.

BROWN-GRANT, K. (1956). *J. Physiol. (Lond.)*, **131**, 52.

BROWN-GRANT, K. (1960). *Brit. med. Bull.*, **16**, 165.

BROWN-GRANT, K., EULER, C. VON, HARRIS, G. W., and REICHLIN, S. (1954a). *J. Physiol. (Lond.)*, **126**, 1.

BROWN-GRANT, K., HARRIS, G. W., and REICHLIN, S. (1957). *J. Physiol. (Lond.)*, **136**, 364.

BROWN-GRANT, K., HARRIS, G. W., and REICHLIN, S. (1954b). *J. Physiol. (Lond.)*, **126**, 29.

CROSSON, J., FALCH, J., and REICHLIN, S. (1960). *Endocrinology*, **66**, 777.

EULER, C. VON, and HOLMGREN, B. (1956a). *J. Physiol. (Lond.)*, **131**, 137.

EULER, C. VON, and HOLMGREN, B. (1956b). *J. Physiol. (Lond.)*, **131**, 125.

FORD, D. H., and GROSS, J. (1958). *Endocrinology*, **62,** 416.

GREER, M. A. (1957). *Recent Progr. Hormone Res.*, **13,** 67.

GUILLEMIN, R., YAMAZAKI, E., GARD, D. A., JUTISZ, M., and SAKIZ, E. (1963). *Endocrinology*, **73,** 564.

GUILLEMIN, R., YAMAZAKI, E., JUTISZ, M., and SAKIZ, E. (1962). *C.R. Acad. Sci. (Paris)*, **55,** 1018.

HARRIS, G. W. (1964). This volume, p. 3.

HARRISON, T. S. (1961). *Endocrinology*, **68,** 466.

KHAZIN, A., and REICHLIN, S. (1961). *Endocrinology*, **68,** 914.

LIPSCOMB, H., HATHWAY, D., and GARD, D. (1961). *Clin. Res.*, **9,** 29.

LOWRY, O. H., ROSEBROUGH, N. J., FARR, A. L., and RANDALL, R. J. (1951). *J. biol. Chem.*, **193,** 265.

McCLURE, J. N., and REICHLIN, S. (1964). *Fed. Proc.* **23,** 109.

McKENZIE, J. M. (1958). *Endocrinology*, **63,** 372.

McKENZIE, J. M. (1961). *J. clin. Endocr.*, **21,** 635.

PORATH, J., and SCHALLY, A. V. (1962). *Endocrinology*, **70,** 738.

REICHLIN, S. (1957). *Endocrinology*, **60,** 470.

REICHLIN, S. (1960). *Endocrinology*, **66,** 340.

REICHLIN, S. (1963*a*). *New Engl. J. Med.*, **269,** 1182, 1246, 1296.

REICHLIN, S. (1963*b*). *In* Thyrotropin, p. 56, ed. Werner, S. C. Springfield: Thomas.

REICHLIN, S., and BOSHANS, R. L. (1963). *Fed. Proc.*, **22,** 572.

SALMON, S., UTIGER, R., PARKER, M., and REICHLIN, S. (1962). *Endocrinology*, **70,** 459.

SCHINDLER, W. J., and HARRIS, G. W. (1963). *Fec. Proc.*, **22,** 622.

SCHREIBER, V., ECKERTOVA, A., FRANK, Z., RYBACK, M., GREGOROVA, I., KMENTOVA, V., and JIRGL, V. (1963). *Physiol. bohemoslov.*, **12,** 1.

SHIBUSAWA, K., NISHI, K., and ABE, C. (1959). *Endocr. jap.*, **6,** 31.

STRÖM, G. (1960). *In* Handbook of Physiology, p. 1173, Sect. 1, Vol. 2. Washington, D.C.: American Physiological Society.

WISLOCKI, G. B., and KING, S. L. (1936). *Amer. J. Anat.*, **58,** 421.

YAMADA, T., and GREER, M. A. (1959). *Endocrinology*, **64,** 559.

YAMAZAKI, E., SAKIZ, E., and GUILLEMIN, R. (1963). *Experientia (Basel)*, **19,** 480.

DISCUSSION

Brown-Grant: In your experiments with the small molecular weight fraction you looked at the levels of radioactivity in the blood of these assay mice. Was there in fact any discharge of radioactivity from the thyroid? These extracts might be affecting the peripheral rate of metabolism of thyroxine.

Reichlin: Yes, indeed they might, but I don't think that a change in peripheral thyroxine metabolism would account for the rise in blood radioactivity. Your point with respect to decrease in expected fall of radioactivity is certainly valid.

Brown-Grant: You could, for instance, thyroidectomize the mouse, give it radioactive thyroxine, and then examine the effect of the extract on the peripheral level of thyroxine.

What did your mice look like after they had had 3 mg. of extract injected intravenously?

Reichlin: Three mg. of the large molecular weight protein fraction would be lethal for them, but they tolerate the small molecular weight fraction very well.

Brown-Grant: In the Anatomy Department at Oxford, Professor M. X. Zarrow and I have been looking for an effect of a crude acid extract of median eminence on LH release and ovulation in immature rats primed with pregnant mare's serum gonadotropin and injected with chlor-promazine to block spontaneous LH release. At first we gave the extract intravenously but we had to give this up as it proved to be quite toxic by this route. We had thought it was probably the small molecular weight stuff, the histamine perhaps, that was upsetting the animals, so it is nice to know that we have some hope of getting a less disturbing but still active extract when we get rid of the large molecular weight material.

Florsheim: You mentioned experiments in which you continued cooling for seven to eight hours, and the thyroidal release curve kept its increased slope throughout that time. Dr. Andersson finds that this occurs for only four to six hours in goats. Did this happen in just one animal, Dr. Reichlin? Can you keep this effect up for long periods of time?

Reichlin: The time of eight hours was conditioned by our ability to maintain the animal's cooling apparatus. Persistent thyroid activation for eight hours was observed in several animals.

Harris: Has anybody studied the effect of cooling the anterior pituitary gland?

Andersson: I don't think so.

Harris: Could the thyroxine feedback effects seen, and their obliterating action on neural influences, possibly be due to the large dosage of thyroxine used? In the physiological range of blood thyroxine perhaps the neural influences would not be abolished. But if the dose goes above this physio-logical concentration, whatever that is, perhaps one then gets into the range of pharmacological blunderbusses?

Reichlin: This is a critical point. As physiologists we tend to choose dosages for hormones which will work consistently. We are inclined to use very high and very low doses, and I believe that the pituitary sensitiza-tion to thyroxine concentration occurs over a very narrow range. For example a drop in PBI from $5 \cdot 2$ to $4 \cdot 0 \mu g./100$ ml. will trigger the TSH response in the rat (Lang, S., and Reichlin, S. [1961]. *Proc. Soc. exp. Biol. (N.Y.)*, **108,** 789).

Harris: What dose of thyroxine did you find was the optimum one for the TRF effect?

Reichlin: We got the best response when we used only $5 \mu g.$ thyroxine

2*

as the sole preliminary treatment, given five hours after the injection of ^{131}I, the whole assay being done three days later. The physiological requirement for thyroxine for a mouse must be in the neighbourhood of $0 \cdot 5$ to $1 \cdot 0$ μg. per day, judging from other criteria, so that the 5 μg. is probably not excessive if one considers such things as the rate of distribution and rate of excretion of excessive dosage of thyroxine after a single injection. The critical experiment that has to be done is to determine a dose-response curve to TRF by changing the thyroxine concentration within the pituitary. One can then say that there is an interaction, as has been postulated, but this is quite a difficult experiment. A complementary experiment would be to measure dose-response curves to changing doses of TRF at fixed levels of thyroxine.

HYPOTHALAMIC TEMPERATURE AND
THYROID ACTIVITY

BENGT ANDERSSON

Department of Physiology, Kungl. Veterinärhögskolan, Stockholm

PRESENT knowledge of the nervous control of endocrine activity derives largely from the fundamental studies of Harris and co-workers (cf. Harris, 1948, 1955) showing that nervous stimuli influence the secretion of pituitary tropic hormones via the hypothalamus and a humoral link in the hypothalamo-hypophysial portal vessels. Such a mechanism is apparently responsible for the accelerated release of thyrotropic hormone (TSH) at low temperatures since the expected increased secretion of thyroid hormones on cold exposure no longer occurs in animals whose anterior pituitary is transplanted into the eye (von Euler and Holmgren, 1956). This activation of the hypothalamo-pituitary-thyroid system is apparently not of any major importance for the immediate defence reaction against a sudden cold stress. The acute increase in non-shivering heat production seems rather to be the consequence of increased sympathico-adrenomedullary activity. An increased release of thyroid hormones may instead be of importance during cold acclimation since thyroxine potentiates the calorigenic effect of adrenaline and noradrenaline (cf. Carlson, 1960; Hart, 1963). This synergism between thyroxine and sympathomimetic amines in the promotion of increased non-shivering heat production offers one example of the complex interplay between various thermoregulatory factors, both hormonal and neural, which is necessary for the maintenance of thermal homoeostasis.

Peripheral cold receptors and central "warmth detectors" play essential rôles in the neural control of body temperature. The classical experiments of Magoun and co-workers (1938) focused interest on the preoptic/anterior hypothalamic region as a site for central "warmth detectors". The importance of this part of the brain as a "heat loss centre" has been further elucidated by experiments in various species. Recently more direct evidence for the presence in the rostral hypothalamus of elements specifically sensitive to warmth has been provided by microelectrode studies (Nakayama *et al.*, 1963). The latter studies indicate that some of the warmth detectors are partially active even at brain temperatures considerably below normal, and that the activity increases with rise in temperature to levels much above normal. The "heat loss centre" not only serves to activate physical heat loss mechanisms like peripheral vasodilatation, sweating and polypnoeic breathing; it also exerts a brake on neural cold defence mechanisms, especially shivering (Hemingway *et al.*, 1940; Andersson, Grant and Larsson, 1956). The sensitivity of the heat loss centre is reduced by the inflow from peripheral cold receptors (Andersson, Persson and Ström, 1960; Ingram and Whittow, 1962). Using direct calorimetry, Benzinger and co-workers (cf. Benzinger, Kitzinger and Pratt, 1963) have shown that a similar interplay between central warmth detectors and peripheral cold receptors operates in thermoregulation in man.

In most studies of hormonal cold defence mechanisms a lowering of the external temperature, causing little or no change in the core temperature, has been used as the experimental stimulus. The relative importance of central warmth detectors as compared with that of peripheral cold receptors in the control of non-shivering heat production, therefore, has been difficult to assess. It has however been suggested (Harris and Woods, 1958) that the preoptic heat loss centre may influence the secretion of TSH via the median eminence and tuber cinereum.

Over the past few years our attention has been directed to studying the rôle of the heat loss centre in the integration of neural and hormonal thermoregulatory mechanisms and also in alimentation. The experiments have been performed in unanaesthetized goats, and some of the results will be briefly reviewed here.

PRINCIPAL METHODS OF STUDY

Since in these studies interest was focused predominantly on the importance of the heat loss centre in the integration of neural and hormonal thermoregulatory mechanisms, relatively few experiments were performed in a purposely altered external temperature. The goats were routinely kept tied up in metabolism cages at a room temperature of $18 \pm 3°$ c. Most experiments involving

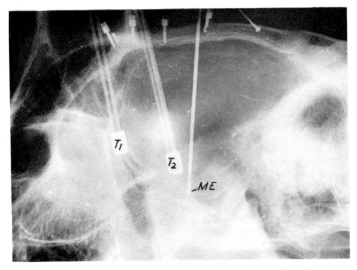

FIG. 1. X-ray picture of the head of a goat with one thermode (T_1) permanently implanted in the forebrain and another (T_2) medially in the preoptic/
anterior hypothalamic region. In addition two parallel thermocouple
electrodes were implanted with the uninsulated tips placed bilaterally in the
median eminence (ME). Local cooling via thermode T_1 caused no rise in
body temperature and no thyroid activation. Local cooling via T_2 caused
the expected marked rise in core temperature and thyroid activation. The
thyroid response to central cooling was completely blocked after lesioning
the median eminence by RF-heating between the electrode tips. (From
Andersson et al., 1963a.)

To face p. 37.

local cooling or warming of the preoptic/anterior hypothalamic region were also made in this, their normal position and customary environment, to avoid disturbing effects of changed external conditions. On some occasions, however, it was of interest to study also the influence of external heat or cold. Then the experiments were performed in a heat chamber or in a cold room. A more rapid and intense cold stimulus was also induced in some cases by administration of large volumes of ice water into the rumen.

Local cooling or warming of the preoptic/anterior hypothalamic region was performed with no extra restraint of the animals, as described previously (cf. Andersson et al., 1963a). Thus central cooling was accomplished by perfusing with cold water a silver thermode permanently implanted medially in the preoptic/anterior hypothalamic region (Fig. 1, T_2). Similar water-perfused thermodes were also originally used for local warming of the preoptic/anterior hypothalamic region. In later experiments more uniform warming of this region was accomplished by radio-frequency (RF) heating between two bilaterally implanted silver plates. Lesions in the median eminence were made in unanaesthetized, thermode-bearing goats by RF-heating between the tips of two permanently implanted needle electrodes (Fig. 1, ME).

Thyroid function was studied by use of [131]I. Thyroidal uptake and release of ^{131}I and plasma protein-bound [131]I (PBI[131]) were followed (cf. Andersson et al., 1963a). The disappearance rate of tracer doses of labelled thyroxine and tri-iodothyronine was also studied in some experiments involving local cooling of the heat loss centre (Andersson et al., 1964a).

In the series of experiments in which the release of sympatho-mimetic amines was studied (Andersson et al., 1964b, c), the level of adrenaline and noradrenaline in the urine was estimated fluorimetrically according to the procedure described by von Euler and Lishajko (1961).

RESULTS

Only the results of studies of the interaction between the heat loss centre and the pituitary-thyroid and the sympathico-adrenomedullary systems will be considered here. A more general account of the thermoregulatory and alimentary effects of local cooling and warming of the rostral hypothalamus in the goat may be found elsewhere (cf. Andersson, Gale and Sundsten, 1962c, 1964d).

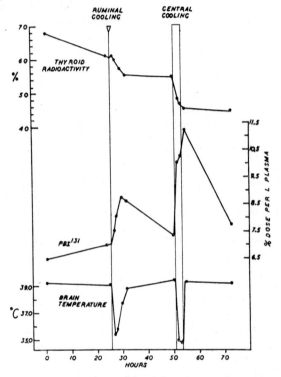

FIG. 2. A comparison of thyroid activation obtained by ruminal cooling and local cooling of the "heat loss centre" in a goat. Brain temperature recorded 3 mm. lateral to the thermode. Ruminal cooling was accomplished by giving 0·12 l. of ice water/kg. body weight by stomach tube. Room temperature 19° C. (From Andersson *et al.*, 1962a.)

Cooling of the "heat loss centre". Local cooling of the preoptic/anterior hypothalamic region invariably produced thyroid (Andersson *et al.*, 1962a, 1963a) and sympathico-adrenomedullary (Andersson *et al.*, 1964c) activation concomitant with the development of marked hyperthermia. Increased thyroid activity was evidenced by an often conspicuous rise in plasma PBI^{131} and a corresponding fall in thyroid radioactivity (Fig. 2). The rise in plasma PBI^{131} became apparent after 30 min. but the steepest rise generally occurred between 30 and 150 min. after the onset of central cooling. Therefore, if the preoptic/anterior hypothalamic region was locally cooled for less than 30 min. no rise in plasma PBI^{131} was observed until after the actual cooling period. When relatively short periods of central cooling (two to three hours) were repeated at intervals of 21 to 22 hours, a thyroid response of about the same magnitude was obtained each time. During prolonged periods of preoptic/anterior hypothalamic cooling the plasma PBI^{131} reached a maximum after four to six hours and then started to decline. Although declining, it remained well above the expected normal slope of the plasma PBI^{131} curve during the entire period of central cooling. When cooling was stopped, the plasma PBI^{131} returned to or fell below the expected normal value.

The decline in plasma PBI^{131} level appearing during prolonged cooling of the heat loss centre could be due to accelerated utilization of thyroidal hormones, to an inhibitory "feedback" action of these hormones on TSH secretion, or to a combination of both. The use of labelled exogenous thyroxine and tri-iodothyronine did not give any indication of accelerated utilization of thyroidal hormones during $1\frac{1}{2}$ to 2 hours of central cooling (Andersson *et al.*, 1964*a*). The administration of exogenous thyroxine was, however, found to block the thyroidal response to local cooling of the heat loss centre (Andersson, Gale and Ohga, 1963*b*). The intravenous injection of 15 μg./kg. body weight of thyroxine was thus found to have completely blocked the thyroidal response to central cooling after two hours (Fig. 3). However, 15 to 20 min. after the administration of thyroxine, this blockage was still largely incomplete, suggesting that an accumulation of thyroxine has to occur at some site before a full inhibition of TSH release is obtained. A gradual saturation of a median eminence "filtering off" mechanism of the kind suggested by Brown-Grant (1957) may perhaps be the explanation of this phenomenon.

The blocking effect of exogenous thyroxine on the thyroidal response to local cooling of the heat loss centre indicates that the latter response is secondary to accelerated release of TSH and suggests that the depression of the thyroidal response during prolonged central cooling may be a feedback effect. More direct evidence that the thyroidal effect of preoptic/anterior hypothalamic cooling is mediated via the hypothalamo-pituitary-thyroid axis was obtained by studying the effect of median eminence lesions in thermode-bearing goats (Andersson *et al.*, 1963*a*). In

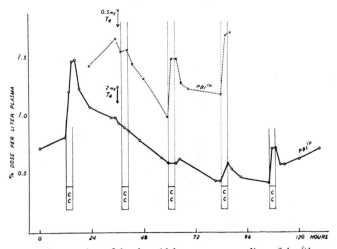

FIG. 3. Suppression of the thyroidal response to cooling of the "heat loss centre" by injection of thyroxine.

Lower curve: The first 3-hour period of central cooling (cc) evoked the usual conspicuous rise in plasma PBI[131]. The response to identical cooling the following day, performed 2 hours after the i.v. injection of 2 mg. of thyroxine (T_4), was completely blocked. Note that the depression of the plasma PBI[131] curve after the injection of this large dose of thyroxine continues during the first post-injection period of central cooling and lasts for about 3 days.

Upper curve: A similar but shorter-lasting blockade obtained by the i.v. injection of 0·5 mg. of thyroxine. (From Andersson, Gale and Ohga, 1963*b*.)

these animals lesions of the median eminence completely blocked the thyroidal response to local cooling of the "heat loss centre". The lesioning of the median eminence by RF heating, however, in itself resulted in a conspicuous thyroid activation (Fig. 4). These lesions caused damage to the hypothalamo-hypophysial portal vessel system, leading to central ischaemic necrosis in the adenohypophysis. The impaired vascular supply to parts of the pituitary may rapidly have caused cell damage, resulting in a non-specific release of TSH. Gale's (1964) observation that exogenous thyroxine does not block the immediate thyroidal activation following upon lesioning the median eminence speaks in favour of this concept.

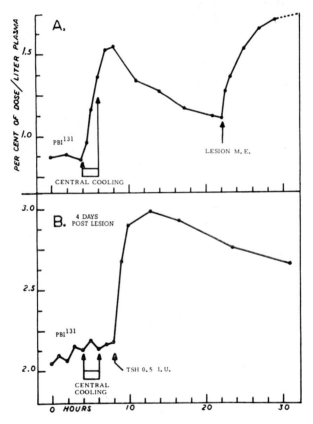

FIG. 4. A. The thyroidal response to local cooling of the "heat loss centre" in a goat before lesioning the median eminence (lesion M.E.). Note the marked thyroid activation also caused by RF-heating of the median eminence. B. The lack of thyroidal response to similar cooling 4 days after the lesion. Note that subsequent injection of TSH caused strong thyroidal activation. (From Andersson *et al.*, 1963*a*.)

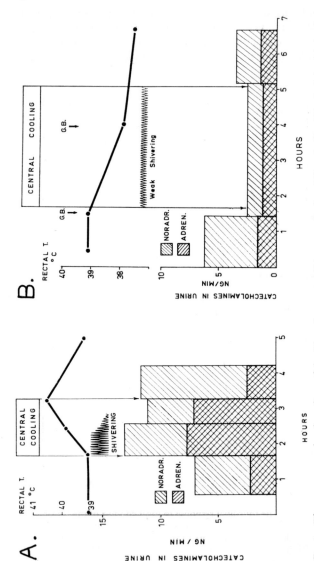

FIG. 5. The response to local cooling of the "heat loss centre" in a goat before (A) and after (B) administration of a ganglionic blocking agent. Note the continued fall in rectal temperature, the diminished excretion of catecholamines and the reduced shivering response after administration of the ganglionic blocking agent, chlorisondamine (Ecolid). GB = i.v. injections of chlorisondamine (0·2 and 0·1 mg./kg.). (From Andersson et al., 1964b.)

During local cooling of the preoptic/anterior hypothalamic region urinary excretion of catecholamines was increased, indicating activation of the sympathico-adrenomedullary system

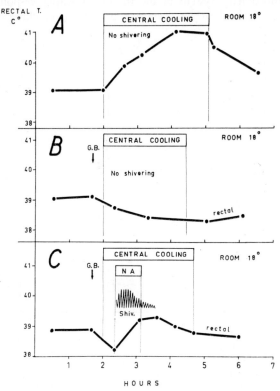

FIG. 6. The response to local cooling of the "heat loss centre" in the goat before (A) and after the administration of a ganglionic blocking agent (B) and the restoration of the response to central cooling by *l*-noradrenaline infusion during ganglionic blockade (C). Note that central cooling *per se* did not induce shivering at this room temperature (18° C) (A and B) but did so during the infusion of *l*-noradrenaline (C). GB = i.v. injection of the ganglionic blocking agent, chlorisondamine (0·3 mg./kg.). NA = Period of *l*-noradrenaline infusion (initial injection of 3 μg./kg. followed by infusion at a rate of 0·5 μg./kg./min.). (From Andersson *et al.*, 1964*b*.)

(Andersson *et al.*, 1964*c*) (Fig. 5A). The relative increase of adrenaline excretion was considerably greater than that of noradrenaline
excretion. To evaluate further the importance of the sympathico-
adrenmoedullary system in the thermoregulatory response to
cooling of the heat loss centre a ganglionic blocking agent

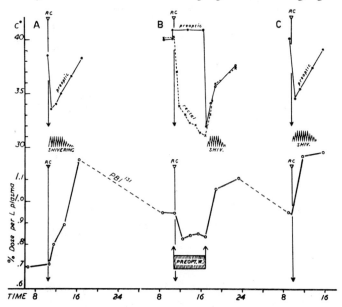

FIG. 7. Blocking of the thyroid response to a general cold stress by local
warming of the "heat loss centre". A. Thyroid response (plasma PBI[131])
to ruminal cooling (RC). B. Inhibition of this response by preoptic warming
(preopt. w.) to about 41° C. Note subsequent rise in plasma PBI[131] and
onset of shivering when preoptic warming was stopped. C. Ruminal cooling repeated without preoptic warming. Time of day recorded on abscissa.
From Andersson *et al.*, 1962*b*.)

(chlorisondamine: Ecolid, CIBA) was used (Andersson *et al.*,
1964*b*). The ganglionic blocking prevented the rise in body
temperature which normally occurs during local cooling of the
heat loss centre. The shivering response to such cooling was
markedly reduced, and, instead of the usual rise in urinary excretion of adrenaline and noradrenaline, catecholamine excretion
remained below normal levels (Fig. 5B). The thyroid activation

obtained by local cooling of the heat loss centre was, however, not altered by the ganglionic blockade. An intravenous infusion of *l*-noradrenaline or adrenaline (0·5 μg./kg./min.) counteracted the

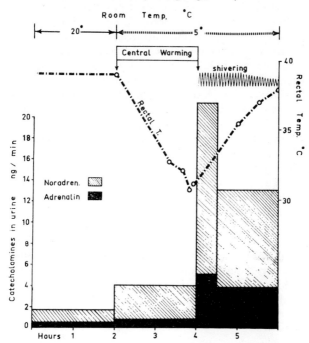

Fig. 8. Inhibition of the sympathico-adrenomedullary response to cold by local warming of the "heat loss centre". Local warming of the preoptic/anterior hypothalamic region simultaneously with sudden exposure of a goat to external cold (5° C) elicited peripheral vasodilatation, polypnoea and a gradual fall of core temperature to 31° C. Despite this considerable hypothermia and the cold environment, catecholamine excretion was only slightly elevated so long as central warming lasted. Upon cessation of this warming, strong shivering developed associated with considerable increase in the excretion of both adrenaline and noradrenaline.

effects of the ganglionic blockade on the response to central cooling, and, further, induced marked shivering (Fig. 6).

Repetitive central cooling performed over longer periods of time caused signs of cold acclimation in spite of the fact that the animals were not exposed to a lowered external temperature (Andersson *et al.*, 1964c). For example, the hair growth was stimulated so that animals which were repeatedly cooled centrally developed noticeably thicker coats than other goats maintained under identical external conditions. There was also a reduction of the noradrenaline response the more frequently central cooling was performed in the same animal, and, further, a progressive increase in protein-bound iodine level and a gradual weakening of the shivering response to central cooling occurred.

Warming of the "heat loss centre". Local warming of the preoptic/anterior hypothalamic region influenced the pituitary-thyroid and the sympathico-adrenomedullary systems in the reverse manner to the corresponding cooling. Such warming was found to block the thyroid activation normally occurring during a general cold stress induced by the administration of large amounts of ice water into the rumen (Andersson *et al.*, 1962b) (Fig. 7). Similarly, during local warming of the heat loss centre in a cold environment the urinary excretion of catecholamines remained low but increased considerably on cessation of central warming (Andersson *et al.*, 1964c). Both adrenaline and noradrenaline excretion then rose to high levels if pronounced hypothermia had developed during central warming (Fig. 8). With induction of a milder degree of hypothermia the increase was predominantly in noradrenaline excretion.

DISCUSSION AND CONCLUSIONS

The aim of the studies reviewed here was to investigate the rôle played by central warmth detectors in the control of hormonal mechanisms of importance in heat production. Local cooling of the preoptic/anterior hypothalamic region (likely to block, or at least markedly reduce, the activity of preoptic warmth detectors) was found to activate the pituitary-thyroid and the sympathico-adrenomedullary systems. Local warming of the same region (increasing the activity of central warmth detectors) was found to prevent the activation of these systems normally occurring during a general cold stress.

As judged by the increase in plasma PBI[131] the thyroid activation obtained by central cooling was much more conspicuous than that seen during simple cold exposure in the goat. Ruminal cooling, on the other hand (causing a marked drop in core temperature), was often seen to cause a thyroid activation comparable to that obtained by local cooling of the heat loss centre. A difference was also observed between the effects on the sympathico-adrenomedullary system of mere cold exposure on the one hand, and cold exposure combined with hypothermia or cooling of the heat loss centre, on the other. Although the immediate response to cold exposure is predominantly an increased release of noradrenaline from the adrenergic nerve endings (Leduc, 1961), cooling of the heat loss centre also caused an increase in adrenaline excretion (Fig. 5A). Likewise, on cessation of warming of the heat loss centre in the cold, when profound hypothermia had developed there was a marked increase in both adrenaline and noradrenaline excretion (Fig. 8). At a milder level of hypothermia, however, there was still a marked increase in noradrenaline excretion on cessation of central warming, whereas relatively little increase in adrenaline excretion was observed. Recent microelectrode studies indicate that central warmth detectors in the preoptic region are slightly active at brain temperatures as low as $32° c$, but that their spontaneous discharge increases with increase in brain temperature to $41° c$ (Nakayama et al., 1963). One must therefore consider the possibility that the heat loss centre still exerts some inhibitory tone on cold defence mechanisms at temperatures considerably below normal level. It may also be that a relatively high degree of activity in this "centre" is needed to counteract the stimulatory effect of peripheral cold on adrenergic nerves (noradrenaline secretion), whereas the pituitary-thyroid system and the adrenal medulla (adrenaline secretion) are more readily inhibited. For the further evaluation of the relative importance of peripheral cold receptors and central warmth detectors it would be of particular interest to compare the thyroid and catecholamine response to central cooling in a cold and in a warm environment.

The signs of cold acclimation developing as a consequence of repetitive central cooling being performed over longer periods of time indicate that cold acclimation may occur in spite of there being no lowering of the external temperature, provided the central warmth detectors are repeatedly inactivated. It is in agreement with the observation of Adolph and Richmond (1956) that cold acclimation follows more rapidly on induction of core hypothermia than on simple exposure to cold.

The effect of a ganglionic blockade and its reversal by infusion of sympathomimetic amines (Fig. 6) indicate that an activation of the sympathico-adrenomedullary system is the primary cause of the temperature rise observed during local cooling of the heat loss centre. The thyroid activation *per se* does not seem to be of major importance since it was present to its full extent when the temperature rise was completely inhibited by the administration of the ganglionic blocking agent.

It is of particular interest to compare the effects of an adrenergic and a ganglionic blockade on the response to central cooling in the goat. The adrenergic blockade causes a conspicuous increase in the excretion of sympathomimetic amines and does not prevent the development of considerable hyperthermia during local cooling of the heat loss centre. Rather, the shivering response to such cooling becomes markedly accentuated (Andersson *et al.*, 1964*c*). The ganglionic blockade, on the other hand, reduces catecholamine excretion and prevents the development of hyper-thermia during local cooling of the heat loss centre. It also markedly reduces the shivering response to central cooling (Fig. 5). It seems as if a response by the peripheral effector cells to adrenergic sympathetic impulses is not essential for an acute cold defence, but that the presence of a normal or even elevated level of circulating sympathomimetic amines is needed. The increased thermo-genesis observed as a result of local cooling of the heat loss centre under adrenergic blockade and under ganglionic blockade com-bined with infusion of sympathomimetic amines, may partly be due to the calorigenic action of these amines but also to the apparent facilitatory action of *l*-noradrenaline and adrenaline on the shivering mechanism. The influence of the circulating level of sympathomimetic amines on shivering indicates that not only does central nervous system activity influence hormonal factors of importance in temperature regulation, but that the reverse apparently also occurs.

At present it seems justified to conclude that central warmth detectors in the preoptic/anterior hypothalamic region serve more than merely to mobilize physical heat loss mechanisms during hyperthermia. Even at a normal or slightly lowered brain temperature, they counteract the thermogenic action of peripheral cold by exerting a brake on cold defence mechanisms, both neurogenic (shivering, peripheral vasoconstriction) and hormonal (increased release of pituitary TSH, activation of the sympathico-adrenomedullary system). The strength of this inhibition seems to increase in proportion to the rise in temperature of the heat loss centre, i.e. in proportion to the degree of activation of central warmth detectors.

The repetitive immobilization of central warmth detectors by local cooling may induce cold acclimation in spite of there being no alteration in external temperature.

Catecholamines released in response to cold may in turn act on the central nervous system to facilitate shivering.

SUMMARY

Studies are reviewed of the rôle played by the preoptic "heat loss centre" in the integration of neural and hormonal thermoregulatory mechanisms in unanaesthetized goats.

Local cooling of this "centre" caused conspicuous thyroid activation and increased release of adrenaline and noradrenaline concomitant with the development of considerable hyperthermia. The thyroid response was apparently mediated via release of thyrotropic hormone since it was blocked by exogenous thyroxine and by lesioning the median eminence. Preoptic warming inhibited thyroid and sympathico-adrenomedullary activation normally seen during general cold stress.

It appears that central "warmth detectors" in the preoptic region serve more than merely to mobilize heat loss mechanisms during hyperthermia. Even at normal or slightly lowered brain temperatures, they seem to counteract the thermogenic action of peripheral cold by exerting a brake on cold defence mechanisms, both neurogenic and hormonal. The strength of this inhibition seems to increase as the temperature of the "heat loss centre" rises above normal.

REFERENCES

ADOLPH, E. F., and RICHMOND, J. (1956). *J. appl. Physiol.*, **9**, 53.

ANDERSSON, B., BROOK, A. H., EKMAN, L., and GALE, C. C. (1964a). *Acta physiol. scand.*, in press.

ANDERSSON, B., BROOK, A. H., GALE, C. C., and HÖKFELT, B. (1964b). *Acta physiol. scand.*, in press.

ANDERSSON, B., EKMAN, L., GALE, C. C., and SUNDSTEN, J. W. (1962a). *Life Sciences*, **1**, 1.

ANDERSSON, B., EKMAN, L., GALE, C. C., and SUNDSTEN, J. W. (1962b). *Acta physiol. scand.*, **56**, 94.

ANDERSSON, B., EKMAN, L., GALE, C. C., and SUNDSTEN, J. W. (1963a). *Acta physiol. scand.*, **59**, 12.

ANDERSSON, B., GALE, C. C., HOKFELT, B., and OHGA, A. (1964c). *Acta physiol. scand.*, in press.

ANDERSSON, B., GALE, C. C., and OHGA, A. (1963b). *Acta physiol. scand.*, **59**, 67.

ANDERSSON, B., GALE, C. C., and SUNDSTEN, J. W. (1962c). *Acta physiol. scand.*, **55**, 177.

ANDERSSON, B., GALE, C. C., and SUNDSTEN, J. W. (1964d). *In* Thirst in the Regulation of Body Water, ed. Wayner, M. New York: Pergamon Press. In press.

ANDERSSON, B., GRANT, R., and LARSSON, S. (1956). *Acta physiol. scand.*, **37**, 261.

ANDERSSON, B., PERSSON, N., and STRÖM, L. (1960). *Acta physiol. scand.*, **50**, 54.

BENZINGER, T. H., KITZINGER, C., and PRATT, A. W. (1963). *In* Temperature, its Measurement and Control in Science and Industry, vol. 3, p. 637, ed. Hardy, J. D. New York: Reinhold.

BROWN-GRANT, K. (1957). *Ciba Found. Coll. Endocr.*, **10**, 97. London: Churchill.

CARLSON, L. B. (1960). *Fed. Proc.*, **19**, suppl. 5, 25.

EULER, C. VON, and HOLMGREN, B. (1956). *J. Physiol. (Lond.)*, **131**, 137.

EULER, U. S. VON, and LISHAJKO, F. (1961). *Acta physiol. scand.*, **51**, 348.

GALE, C. C. (1964). *Acta physiol. scand.*, in press.

HARRIS, G. W. (1948). *J. Physiol. (Lond.)*, **107**, 418.

HARRIS, G. W. (1955). Neural Control of the Pituitary Gland. London: Arnold.

HARRIS, G. W., and WOODS, W. (1958). *J. Physiol. (Lond.)*, **143**, 246.

HART, J. S. (1963). *In* Temperature, its Measurement and Control in Science and Industry, vol. 3, p. 373, ed. Hardy, J. D. New York: Reinhold.

HEMINGWAY, A., RASMUSSEN, T., WIKOFF, H., and RASMUSSEN, A. T. (1940). *J. Neurophysiol.*, **3**, 329.

INGRAM, D. L., and WHITTOW, G. C. (1962). *J. Physiol. (Lond.)*, **163**, 211.

LEDUC, J. (1961). *Acta physiol. scand.*, **53**, suppl. 183.

MAGOUN, H. W., HARRISON, F., BROBECK, J. R., and RANSON, S. W. (1938). *J. Neurophysiol.*, **1**, 101.

NAKAYAMA, T., HAMMEL, H. T., HARDY, J. D., and EISENMAN, J. S. (1963). *Amer. J. Physiol.*, **204**, 1122.

DISCUSSION

Harris: What does this increased thyroid function do? The action of thyroxine in the body doesn't begin until 24 hours or so after it has been administered, and here is a mechanism for raising the blood level of thyroxine for a few hours only. I suppose one could argue that the thyroxine triggered something that happened 24 hours later. However, it is curious that a cold stimulus has such a fleeting effect and yet the latent period of action of thyroxine is so long. I suppose this is thinking teleologically, but it seems difficult to fit this into the physiology of the animal.

Andersson: The potentiating action of thyroxine on the calorigenic action of the catecholamines, which has been shown in several studies (see Carlson, 1960, *loc. cit.*), might be of importance of course. Thyroidectomized rats exposed to cold still respond with an increased rate of metabolism although it is insufficient to maintain thermal equilibrium (Swanson, H. [1957]. *Endocrinology,* **60,** 205). A certain basic level of thyroxine may be needed but not any excessive amounts. It has thus been found that cold-acclimated rats maintain thermal equilibrium in the cold on only basal requirements of thyroxine ($2 \cdot 5 \mu g./day$) (Sellers, E. A., and You, S. S. [1950]. *Amer. J. Physiol.,* **163,** 81).

Spence: Tri-iodothyronine comes out as well, I presume, and that acts at once, doesn't it?

Reichlin: Not for six hours anyway.

Andersson: I think it is safe to conclude that the immediate cold defence response is not dependent upon the thyroxine at all.

Reichlin: It is likely that the acute neural, autonomic and adrenergic responses maintain the central core temperature; it is only when they fail that the thyroid responds to cold, and this may be looked upon as a measure of desperation. It is really quite difficult to produce regularly thyroid activation in either rabbits or rats with external cold exposure. I think this is partly because the animal protects its core temperature with every means at its disposal. If we go beyond that and put the cold into the brain itself, we manage to bring on this additional humoral response.

Harris: What does drinking large volumes of cold water do?

Reichlin: That is a very good cold stress but it is quite different from external cooling. Central core cooling does occur after oral ingestion of cold liquids. I was surprised and pleased that Dr. Andersson observed a more marked thyroid response to ruminal cooling than to external cooling.

Andersson: Short-term exposure of goats to external cold generally does not produce observable changes in thyroid activity, but such exposure is not seen to cause any drop in body temperature. Rather, there is a slight increase in rectal temperature, apparently due to shivering and strong peripheral vasoconstriction.

Florsheim: How important do you feel that these effects are in the general control of thyroid function? Van Beugen and van der Werff ten Bosch (1961. *Acta endoc.* (*Kbh.*), **37,** 470) ablated much of the forebrain and found no effect on the response to cold stress and no effect on thyroid function. They also found that lesions obliterating the rostral edge of the "thyrotropin area" do not prevent thyroid activation by cold stress (1961. *Acta endocr.* (*Kbh.*), **38,** 585). Others (see Kovács, S., Vértes, M., and Kövesi, G. [1960]. *Acta physiol. Acad. Sci. hung.*, **17,** 295) have made rather extensive lesions in the posterior hypothalamus, where presumably the effector neurones for cold response are located, and they got no effect on thyroid function. In all your experiments you measured only the most sensitive criterion of thyroid function: an increase in the PBI[131] measures about the smallest change in TSH secretion that can be detected by laboratory tests. These are very small modifying actions and they may be of limited physiological importance.

Andersson: Does anyone nowadays think that there are any central cold detectors in the posterior hypothalamus?

Florsheim: There are no detectors there; there are effectors.

Andersson: We found that cooling the posterior hypothalamus has more or less the opposite effect—inhibition of the shivering response to external cold, probably because the effectors of the cold response are inactivated to a certain extent (Andersson *et al.*, 1963, *loc. cit.*).

Florsheim: There may be one system which can go either way, or there may be two detector systems in the anterior hypothalamus; there doesn't seem to be any real agreement on whether there are neurones sensitive to cold and neurones sensitive to heat there, or whether it is the same neurone that is affected differently at different temperatures. The cold-detecting system seems to require posterior hypothalamic co-operation to produce its effect. The heat-sensitive neurones, if they are different, have their effectors right in the preoptic area, so I would expect lesions in the posterior hypothalamic area to have an effect on thyroid function, because you are unbalancing an equilibrium state.

Brown-Grant: I don't think the experiments of van Beugen and van der Werff ten Bosch that you referred to are really comparable to Dr. Andersson's work. In one series of experiments they removed the entire forebrain as far back as the anterior commissure (1961. *Acta endocr.* (*Kbh.*), **37,** 470) and in the others they placed lesions in the anterior basal hypothalamus that reduced the resting level of thyroid activity (1961. *Acta endocr.* (*Kbh.*), **38,** 585), and then exposed their animals for a matter of weeks in the cold. It is fairly well known now that rats in the cold eat more and that the whole of the thyroxine metabolism of the rat may be very closely related to the amount of food it eats and the amount of thyroxine it loses in the faeces. I think that what van Beugen and van der Werff ten Bosch observed was a very indirect activation of the thyroid consequent upon a fall in blood thyroxine level caused by an increased rate of peripheral metabolism of thyroxine in the cold together with an increased food intake and increased faecal loss of thyroxine. If the cold response of their rats had been tested over a four to six-hour period, as in Dr. Andersson's experiments, they would, I suspect, have found an impairment of the thyroid response to cold in the animals with anterior hypothalamic lesions.

Harris: Did they in fact completely remove the supraoptic region of the hypothalamus? If they had, their animals would probably have been blind and I don't think they were.

Florsheim: They went from the bregma down to the optic chiasma. Kovács (Kovács, Vértes and Kövesi, 1960, *loc. cit.*) has done similar experiments where he makes roughly the same cut.

Reichlin: Was the anterior commissure in or not? This is a very important landmark. If the anterior commissure was included within the preserved brain then the central cold receptors are still in the brain.

Florsheim: I think the cut passed through the septum.

Andersson: Nakayama and co-workers (1963, *loc. cit.*) have found these responding neurones in the preoptic region and in a fairly medial position, say a few millimetres to the left or right; this area extends, if you distinguish between the preoptic area and the anterior hypothalamus, slightly into the anterior hypothalamus.

Brown-Grant: Have you looked at corticosteroid excretion or secretion in your goats?

Andersson: Dr. Bernt Hökfelt in the Department of Endocrinology, Karolinska Institutet, has helped us to determine whether cooling affects the cortisol level in the blood. The results are rather confusing. The normal cortisol level is very variable in these animals and we don't see any consistent trend of any increased cortisol level during central cooling. J. Chowers, H. T. Hammel and S. M. McCann (1963. Personal communication), working with dogs, have found an increased cortisol level during the first half-hour of preoptic cooling. We usually took our samples at half-hour intervals, starting before cooling and, say, half an hour later and so on, during the three-hour period of cooling, and we did not see any consistent change. Perhaps urinary excretion of cortisol should be determined at the same time.

Brown-Grant: It might also be done directly with adrenal venous blood sampling from an adrenal gland transplant.

GENERAL DISCUSSION

Brown-Grant: The effect of stress on the thyroid has been mentioned by one or two people here. Some years ago Professor Harris gave a paper on the reciprocal relationships between the thyroid and adrenocortical responses to stress (1955. *Ciba Found. Coll. Endocr.*, **8,** 531. London: Churchill). We have heard today of a lot of ways in which the thyroid can be activated in the laboratory but stress is not one of them. Indeed, in animal experiments the effect of stress is to decrease thyroid activity; yet in the clinical literature it has often been suggested that either acute or chronic psychological stress may be related to hyperfunction of the thyroid gland. What is the current view as to this possibility?

Gibson: There is not much in the literature (cf. review: Gibson, J. G. [1962]. *J. psychosom. Res.*, **6,** 93) to suggest that emotional stress can have a profound effect on thyroid activity—certainly not an effect that is significant to the individual unless there is a family history of hyperthyroidism and the stress is operative over a period of time. Moreover the work that has been done on thyroid function in various psychiatric disorders does not suggest that there is much evidence of either hyperactivity or hypoactivity as a constant feature.

Stevenson: Dr. Brown-Grant has indicated that the increased thyroid activity in these animals was not due to stress. I think that if I were a goat or a rat, in any of the experiments described here, I would regard myself as having been "stressed".

Asher: What has been demonstrated is this, that if you forcibly hold a rat or a goat and push a cold rod into his brain he gets a bit heated; but if you are only pretending the rod is cold, and push a tepid one into his brain —he still gets rather heated about it. So it may be that it is not the coldness of the rod that makes him get hot, but merely that he finds the rod in his brain upsetting and gets heated for that reason.

Reichlin: If the rat is stressed deliberately, by confining it in a small cage and by applying local cooling, there is no thyroid activation. When the rat is unrestrained there is thyroid activation. Dr. Andersson's goats are restrained very lightly and probably not stressed.

Mandelbrote: Last year we had an abnormally cold winter here and clinicians saw many cases suffering from hypothermia. In cases of undetected hypothyroidism this effect of severe cold precipitated some patients into a state of myxoedema coma, which seems to be a little different from the experimental presentation as I understood it, in which cooling in fact accelerates thyroid activity. A further complication is that when Largactil (chlorpromazine) was given to somebody who had undetected hypothyroidism and had been exposed to cold, then a very severe state of hypothermia and myxoedema coma was produced.

Greene: I saw about six hypothermic cases last winter and two of them had obviously been myxoedematous for a very long time, but nobody had done anything about it. These two had been exposed to severe cold for a long time and were brought in unconscious. Another patient had undoubtedly taken an overdose of chlorpromazine and was brought in unconscious. There was no reason to believe that the remaining cases had taken any kind of drug or that they had any previous history of myxoedema. Luckily all these patients survived and I was able to confirm that the two with the previous history of myxoedema were still myxoedematous, but the others were not myxoedematous at all. How can you immediately differentiate between myxoedema plus hypothermia, a drug plus hypothermia, and plain hypothermia?

Mandelbrote: We had only a few cases and were not geared for experimentation. These people were not diagnosed initially as suffering from myxoedema, perhaps because of insufficient clinical acumen, and the investigation only proceeded after the hypothermia had occurred (hypothermia being defined in terms of drop in body temperature), when one could demonstrate through PBI investigations that the patient was suffering from myxoedema. These patients were then treated with some derivative of thyroxine and in the two cases that I am thinking of the thyroid function and the body temperature returned to normal. Incidentally, one of these patients who had been on chlorpromazine, which I think was the precipitant of the coma, was not only suffering from hypothyroidism but was a chronic hallucinated schizophrenic. She remained hallucinated even when her thyroid function and body temperature returned to normal. Then we had to introduce Stelazine (trifluoperazine), which is another phenothiazine derivative, rather cautiously, so that we wouldn't precipitate this whole problem all over again; for some reason this did not disturb either the thyroid function or the body temperature, and it gradually damped down her hallucinatory experience. This woman is now functioning very well with normal thyroid function, without much manifestation of schizophrenia, on treatment with thyroxine derivative and trifluoperazine.

Asher: It seems that this problem is complicated by the fact that some people's thyroids stop working because they get cold and other people get cold because their thyroids stop working.

Stevenson: A possible explanation of why these people were myxoedematous is that during the period of hypothermia an increase of thyroid output had taken place and exhausted the thyroid; thus the patient was temporarily in a state of myxoedema, and was so debilitated that he could not reactivate his own thyroid again.

Something which was said earlier implied that the "central cooling" of the brain centres artificially puts into quick motion a reaction which nature intended to occur in slow motion, and that the rapid thyroid activity seen in experimentally induced hypothermia is, in the natural order, something which would take place slowly. These people when exposed to cold would normally call into play other defence mechanisms first, and the thyroid reaction would be a last effort to deal with the hypothermia. These patients were elderly and would probably have debilitated thyroid function anyway.

Reichlin: In the clinical spectrum of myxoedema coma there are obviously comatose myxoedematous patients who have normal body temperature. There are others who have both coma and low body temperature. A certain proportion will be restored to some kind of normal mental state, or at least an improvement of mental state, by simple warming, which indicates that hypothermia in the presence of thyroxine deficiency can cause coma, and to some extent brain function depends upon both thyroxine and body temperature. I think these two factors are separable. Chlorpromazine has a curious and confusing effect; it interferes further with brain function in an already depressed brain and may convert a mild hypothyroid syndrome to one of quite severe proportions. We have seen, as Dr. Mandelbrote has, a patient without myxoedema in whom gross classical myxoedema has been precipitated by chlorpromazine. The explanation is probably that chlorpromazine has a peripheral effect on thyroxine metabolism. In a project that Dr. Witt and I did three or four years ago, large doses of chlorpromazine were found to double the peripheral thyroxine degradation rate (Reichlin, S., Koussa, M. G. and Witt, F. W. [1959]. *J. clin. Endocr.*, **19**, 692). If a patient had minimum thyroid reserve to begin with, increase in thyroxine degradation could not be compensated for and acute thyroxine insufficiency might be precipitated.

Harris: Would you imply that if you give chlorpromazine, the thyroid activity first goes up?

Reichlin: The overall effect of these substances is complex: if chlorpromazine is given to a human subject in large doses, there is a trivial change in PBI, an increase in thyroxine turnover rate and variable effects on ^{131}I uptake by the thyroid. The effects of a drug like this, which involve central and peripheral phenomena, are very hard to dissociate.

Harris: I certainly agree with that, but there seems little doubt that chlorpromazine has a hypothalamic action—one can quote its effects in producing amenorrhoea and lactation, and so on. I was just wondering what was the central action of chlorpromazine on TSH release.

Reichlin: We studied thyroxine metabolism in a group of psychiatric cases who were on continuous sleep therapy for psychosis. Patients were put to sleep for almost a month, being allowed up for only four hours a day. These people are thoroughly drugged with not only chlorpromazine but Phenergan (promethazine) and similar substances. No changes in the PBI were observed.

Stevenson: We studied thyroid function and chlorpromazine medication at St. Ebba's Hospital for over a year and found they were quite closely linked. The ketosteroids also tended to go down steadily. We came to the conclusion that chlorpromazine acted as a chronic mild stressor in some way.

Greene: What were your criteria of thyroid function?

Stevenson: [131]I uptake, BMR, PBI and serum cholesterol, measured by the methods described by G. H. L. Bullmore and co-workers (1958. *In* Psychoendocrinology, p. 52, ed. Reiss, M. New York and London: Grune & Stratton).

Harris: I am not quite clear. In your experience did thyroid function tend to increase after chlorpromazine therapy?

Stevenson: My colleagues and I think that chlorpromazine medication altered the thyroid function. In rats on chlorpromazine the weights of the thyroid, thymus and ovary decreased, while adrenal weight tended to rise; when daily doses of 4 mg. or more were given the ^{131}I uptake by the thyroid tended to fall at first and then rise above the control values, returning to normal between 20 to 60 days after the start of the treatment (Bullmore *et al.*, 1958, *loc. cit.*; Reiss, M. [1958]. *In* Psychoendocrinology, p. 182).

Jellinek: I am sure we agree with Dr. Stevenson's earlier point, that cold brings out latent hypothyroidism by increasing the secretion of thyroxine, but I would be interested to learn about the converse situation—does fever in fact depress thyroid function? I would also like to hear more about the treatment of hypothermic hypothyroid coma. I remember being very worried over the death of a patient to whom we had given 0·5 mg. of thyroxine intravenously. I thought then that we might have been overtreating her. Now I am not so sure, because apparently treatment with thyroxine is not acutely important in these cases of coma. Dr. Andersson's results imply that these people ought to be treated with adrenaline and noradrenaline. The patient does not die of thyroxine deficiency but because the adrenals do not work efficiently in hypothyroidism. The patients who die from overtreatment with thyroxine do not die until about a fortnight later, of cardiac failure, but I don't think one kills them immediately by overtreating them with thyroid hormones.

Greene: When you give them thyroid hormones of any kind, you presumably increase their sensitivity to the catecholamines, and do good that way.

Jellinek: I think it is fairly generally agreed in the literature that they already have depressed adrenal function, so perhaps one should not really be giving them thyroid at all, unless one gives them adrenaline or noradrenaline at the same time.

3

Reichlin: The clinician is on the horns of a dilemma in these situations. If the brain is desperately short of thyroxine, death may occur at any time, but if a dose of thyroxine is given to a person who has been deficient for a long time he may be killed by the production of cardiac arrhythmia. The literature reports about 50 per cent survivals from myxoedema coma treated with intravenous tri-iodothyronine or thyroxine.

Greene: I have often seen that statement about 50 per cent survivals in myxoedema coma but I don't understand it. It must be a question of dosage. In recent years I have treated six or eight cases of myxoedema coma and not one of them has died. I have given them very small intravenous doses of tri-iodothyronine and also, with no particular theory behind it, I have given them hydrocortisone (cortisol), and they have been warmed up.

Spence: I have only had two cases of hypothermia. One was a myxoedema case which I treated on the lines you have just described, Dr. Greene, and she lived. The other patient did not have myxoedema; she was shown to have syphilitic endarteritis of the vessels of the hypothalamus which was probably interfering with her temperature control.

Rollin: Artificial hypothermia has been used in the treatment of chronic schizophrenics (Hays, P., Woolfson, G., Krikler, B., and Day, B. [1960]. *J. ment. Sci.*, **106,** 344). I am not aware that thyroid studies were done there, but they may have been done in similar studies elsewhere. Therapeutically, from the psychiatric standpoint, the results were negative, but the experiment was interesting.

One phenomenon that we have seen in mental hospitals is the obesity of patients treated with chlorpromazine. Could the physiologists tell us clinicians whether this obesity is the result of hypothermia or of some disturbance of the metabolism?

Reichlin: The spontaneous activity of the patient receiving large doses of chlorpromazine is noticeably diminished. The active, disturbed patient is changed to a relatively quiet, torpid individual. The body temperature falls slightly, even with doses of only a few hundred mg./day, so that I should imagine the overall metabolic rate must fall somewhat. The question you would want us to answer is whether or not food intake is decreased proportionately to the decline in metabolic activity, but I don't believe that this effect has been investigated.

Rollin: This obesity is so indiscriminate in its distribution in the patient population that I don't think your thesis is valid. There has been no complaint from ward sisters that the food intake in any particular ward has gone up because of treatment with chlorpromazine.

Greene: We must remember that a very small, almost unnoticeable, increase in calorie intake (as low as 100 calories a day), with no change in the activity, will ultimately produce obesity.

Mandelbrote: Some of these are mammoth increases. I have seen some patients 50 per cent above their original body weight even if they have been on chlorpromazine for a comparatively short time. This may not be entirely related to increase of appetite and food intake; water metabolism, salt metabolism, and other facets of metabolic disturbance may be relevant here.

Gibson: It is possible that chlorpromazine produces a certain degree of water retention. It is used in the treatment of anorexia nervosa, and the patients, although they may not eat much more, tend to drink more. Also, doesn't chlorpromazine have a hypothermic effect by peripheral vaso-dilatation? This might have an additional physiological effect, together with the muscular hypotonia—there might be a loss of fluid into the tissues, giving rise to an increase in body weight.

Greene: One of the facts which is most frequently denied is that a very large proportion of fat women—I don't know why it should be fat *women* in particular, but I think it is—have a slight but easily demonstrable oedema. That would perhaps explain this gross increase in weight Dr. Rollin was talking about.

EFFECTS OF THYROID HORMONES ON
BRAIN DIFFERENTIATION

J. T. EAYRS

*Institute of Psychiatry, The Maudsley Hospital,
Denmark Hill, London*

THE relationship between thyroid activity and cerebral function in man scarcely needs emphasis, for it is well known that excessive thyroid secretion is associated with hyperexcitability, irritability, restlessness, exaggerated response to environmental stimuli and emotional instability, whereas myxoedema is marked by the insidious onset of listlessness, slowness of speech and mentation, lack of energy and other related symptoms. It is customary to explain these phenomena as the cerebral manifestations of overall changes in bodily metabolism which can be corrected by therapy appropriate for adjusting the level of circulating thyroid hormone to the current needs of the tissues. If metabolic factors alone were involved it would be expected that such changes would prove independent of the time of onset of the dysfunction; but, as has long been recognized, the symptomatology of cretinism differs in important respects from that of both adult and juvenile myxoedema and it has become widely accepted that, when thyroid deficiency arises early in life, the disorder may be irreversible in character and of a severity directly related to such factors as the age of onset, diagnosis and efficacy of treatment. Means (1948) summarizes this position in the words: "If cretinism is recognized in the few months' old infant and adequate thyroid treatment started and maintained without omission throughout life, the chance of normal development is fair even in the face of a totally atrophic thyroid"; and Simpson (1948) says: "If treatment has been delayed for some years the only result may be the conversion of a harmless, apathetic idiot into a mischievous, truculent, troublesome semi-idiot". Since thyroid hormone is known to play an important part in regulating those maturational processes which mark the transition from infant to adult (Allen, 1938; Ray *et al.*, 1950) such a point of view would seem to imply that its absence may impose some form of permanent abnormality upon the growth of the brain.

Clinical observations, however, have from time to time thrown doubt upon this interpretation. While there is no dispute concerning the association of severe mental retardation with congenital hypothyroidism, there is less agreement on whether the defects are to be attributed directly to the influence of thyroid deficiency on cerebral maturation and, where the institution of therapy is concerned, on the importance to be attached to the time factor. For instance, in an extensive survey in which the fullest available information concerning the patients' own and family histories was taken into account, Lewis (1937a, b) concluded that, while promptness and adequacy of treatment were important factors determining recovery, they were not decisive. In some cases, diagnosed early and treated continuously, the subjects remained defective: in others, in spite of late diagnosis and/or sporadic treatment, the intelligence quotient was close to the normal range. Substantially the same general findings have been reported by others (e.g. Bruch and McCune, 1944; Radwin et al., 1949), although it is generally conceded that IQ's above 100 in treated cretins are rare indeed and that the highest that can confidently be predicted is about 70 (Brown, Bronstein and Kraines, 1939). On the other hand, in a more recent study of 128 cases, Smith, Blizzard and Wilkins (1957) were impressed by a high correlation both between the age of onset of hypothyroidism, the commencement of treatment and the subsequent IQ of the patient. At the same time, however, these observers conceded that many patients who were adequately treated failed to respond.

Three types of explanation can be adduced to explain such anomalies. The first takes account of the possibility that not all the relevant information is available to the clinician analysing the data. Possible faulty initial diagnoses and the notorious failure of outpatients rigidly to adhere to regimens of prescribed treatment (Horn, 1954) may well be concealed. A second class of explanation stems from uncertainties concerning the time of onset of thyroid deficiency in utero, the titre of thyroid hormone needed to maintain normal cerebral development during this period of life and the extent to which, in man, trans-placental maternal hormone can compensate for foetal deficiency (see Osorio and Myant, 1960). Thus a conceivable differentiation into "responding" and "non-responding" cretins could be made on the grounds that, in some instances of congenital disorder, a small amount of thyroid tissue could secrete enough hormone for early development but be quite inadequate postnatally. The completely athyroid individual, on the other hand, would be exposed to the effects of deficiency considerably earlier during the course of development (McGirr and Hutchison, 1955). Finally there is the possibility, first suggested by Tredgold (1929), that cretins not responding to therapy are those in whom the endocrine condition is superimposed upon a genetically linked primary amentia. As Benda (1947) has pointed out, no hormonal therapy, however adequate, can be expected to raise the mental capacity of the individual above his genetically determined endowment and the failure of thyroid therapy would, in such instances, give the appearance of irreversibility, greater success being obtained where an uncomplicated thyroid deficiency alone was involved. Such an interpretation has, however, been challenged on the grounds that frequently no family history of amentia is found in cretins not responding to treatment (Brown, Bronstein and Kraines, 1939).

EXPERIMENTAL APPROACH

It is perhaps surprising that, outside a few scattered accounts (e.g. Isenschmid, 1918; Lotmar, 1933; Benda, 1947), the problems underlying these observations have failed until recently to capture the attention of the experimental neurologist. A certain amount of information is, however, available from the study of the rat. This species proves to be particularly suitable for an examination of the developmental effects of thyroid deficiency by reason of the relatively undifferentiated state of its brain at the time of birth. This renders it accessible for study at a stage of development when, in other species including man, the organism is confined to the uterus. Moreover, the physical development of the rat is extremely susceptible to departures from the euthyroid state and animals made athyroid from the day of birth are, as is man (Gesell, Amatruda and Culotta, 1936), retarded in the maturation of innately organized behaviour (Eayrs and Lishman, 1955). For example the capacity to land on the feet when dropped back downwards, which appears in the normal rat at about 16 days of age, is delayed until the 24th day in the cretin. This capacity may be regarded as resulting from the complex integration at mesen-cephalic level of visual, labyrinthine and proprioceptive stimuli and the delay suggests that the maturation of the mechanisms responsible has been impaired. On these findings alone the possible influence of a reduced peripheral sensitivity and sluggish motor reactions attributable to metabolic factors cannot be excluded, but a second example would seem to confirm that the development of a central integrative mechanism is involved. When the tail of an infant rat is compressed the animal is thrown into convulsive, poorly co-ordinated activity, the disappearance of which, with advancing age, reflects the maturation of an inhibitory influence by higher centres (Tilney, 1933). This process is likewise delayed in hypothyroidism, although in this instance a reduction in activity due to an impaired metabolism might be expected to oppose the central effects.

The physical and neural effects of neonatal thyroid deficiency in the rat are thus so similar to those in man as to give reason to believe that further studies of development in this species might yield information concerning the cerebral changes underlying the mental retardation of cretinism. These have been pursued by the use of neuroanatomical, neurophysiological and behavioural techniques.

NEUROANATOMICAL CONSIDERATIONS

As a result of hypothyroidism induced experimentally during infancy, the brain besides being reduced in size is changed in shape to the extent that its infantile proportions tend to be maintained (Eayrs and Taylor, 1951). The reason for this would seem to be that endochondral ossification affecting growth at the base of the skull is far more adversely influenced by thyroidectomy than is the membranous ossification of the calvarium and the brain is thus able to grow in height and width but not in length (Dye and Maugham, 1929). This suggests that the symptoms of cretinism may, in part at least, be attributable to a disparity between the growth of brain and cranium, as a result of which nervous tissues become compressed and intracranial pressure raised.

Some support for this view comes from a study of the changes in the pattern of vascularity found in the brain of the cretinoid rat (Eayrs, 1954). Although the relative proportion of cortical tissue occupied by blood vessels is unchanged the distribution of these vessels is modified to the extent that the blood is contained in a relatively smaller number of vessels of larger diameter. An increase in intracranial pressure to a level above that of the normal venous pressure could thus account for some of the vascular changes by impeding the venous return and giving rise to vascular engorgement. A restricted circulation of this kind could give rise to conditions of anoxia which might well be responsible for maturational impairment and for the type of change earlier described by Benda (1947), in the brain of the human cretin, as characteristic of anorexia or anaemic asphyxia. It must, however, be conceded that attempts to demonstrate such an increased intracranial pressure by means of a needle inserted into the cisterna magna have not proved successful (Eayrs, 1956).

The changed pattern of vascularity assumes additional significance, however, for an increased capillary spacing must place some tissue at a nutritional disadvantage. Added to this is the fact that a system composed of a large number of small vessels presents a greater capillary surface available for metabolic exchange than one of similar volume made up of a small number of larger vessels (in the experimental measurements a factor of 2 was involved). These findings are of special interest in so far as *in vitro* measurements of the oxygen consumption of hypothyroid brain do not differ from normal (Fazekas, Graves and Alman, 1951), whereas a fall and not a rise in differences between arterial and venous oxygen tension initially accompanies an increase in the rate of cerebral circulation (Himwich *et al.*, 1942). This conforms with the anatomical data in the sense that the tissues cannot take up oxygen to their full capacity since the capillary bed is inadequately organized to enable them to do so. Recently developed polarographic techniques could prove of great value in the elucidation of possible changes in oxygen tension and their relationship to the influence of thyroid hormone during development.

Further structural changes in the brain of the cretinoid individual concern the size of neurones and the growth and disposition of their processes. The perikarya of neurones located in the sensori-motor cortex are reduced in size and more closely packed in the tissues of the cretinoid rat (Eayrs and Taylor, 1951). This increased density is not due solely to the reduction in mean size, but also partly to a hypoplasia of both axons and dendrites (Eayrs, 1955). The density of axons is reduced throughout the cortical thickness but not in direct relationship to the densities in individual laminae. Layer 4, which receives the specific afferent thalamic plexuses, is differentially affected in a manner which cannot be ascribed to the retardation of a normal growth pattern. Dendrites are shorter and branch less, the combined influences of these two effects being to steepen the rate of decay of dendritic density with distance from the centre of the perikarya and to modify its normally exponential course. Combination of the data for axons and dendrites in the manner described by Uttley (1955) to give an estimate of the probability of axo-dendritic interaction reveals that this factor is dramatically reduced.

NEUROPHYSIOLOGICAL CONSIDERATIONS

It might be expected that these neuroanatomical changes would be reflected in the electrical activity of nervous tissues and this has proved to be the case. Bradley, Eayrs and Schmalbach (1960) showed that the amplitude of the electroencephalogram taken from conscious and unrestrained animals was reduced in neonatally thyroidectomized animals and that the capacity of the cortex to "block" in response to auditory stimuli or to "follow" the frequency of rhythmic photic stimulation was absent or delayed in appearance. These phenomena were not observed in animals thyroidectomized later in life. This failure of sensory input to desynchronize or to synchronize cortical rhythms may perhaps be equated with the hypoplasia of axonal afferent plexuses observed in neurohistological studies.

Further light on the significance of the reduced amplitude of the records taken from cretinoid rats has come from the study of evoked potentials. The negative waves recorded at the cortical surface following stimulation of mid-line (non-specific) thalamic nuclei were increased in latency and duration but reduced in amplitude (Bradley et al., 1961). These effects could not be attributed to differences in the effectiveness of the parameters of stimulation used in the two classes of rat (Bradley, Eayrs and Richards, 1964), but whereas the changes in the temporal parameters of the response could be rectified by semi-acute administration of thyroid hormone, amplitude could not. Moreover, in rats thyroidectomized during adult life the latency and duration of the evoked potential were extended as in the cretinoid animal but amplitude was unaffected. These findings suggest that the time-relationships of electrocortical activity may be related primarily to metabolic factors and amplitude primarily to the processes of growth and maturation. Current concepts concerning the genesis of the slow potentials associated with electrocortical activity lay emphasis on the part played by the summation of post-synaptic dendritic potentials (Clare and Bishop, 1955; 1959) and it is tempting to infer that the reduced amplitude of the records in the neonatally thyroidectomized rat, but not in the animal thyroidectomized when mature, may be attributed to a comparable reduction in the probability of axo-dendritic inter-action as the source of setting up and maintaining these potentials.

BEHAVIOURAL CONSIDERATIONS

The effect of thyroid deficiency on adaptive behaviour as opposed to that on the innately organized type of response considered earlier has been studied in a number of experiments. In the earlier literature, reviewed by Eayrs and Levine (1963), it is generally agreed that thyroidectomy performed on the adult rat is without significant effect on capacity for learning, although the rate of performance may be reduced. In the neonatally thyroidectomized rat, however, the situation is very different. Such animals become more readily habituated to a novel situation and, where habituation plays an important part in the process of learning, the cretinoid rat may compare well with the normal. In more complex situations the cretinoid animal makes many more errors, spending less time on exploratory activity as a result of each error (Eayrs and Lishman, 1955) and appearing to be less sensitive to minor environmental change. Further experiments, using the Hebb-Williams closed-field test (Eayrs, 1961) in which the significance of the time factor is minimal, have shown that the number of errors made during a fixed number of trials is directly related to the age at which thyroidectomy is carried out: the performance of rats made athyroid at birth was considerably worse than that of littermate controls, while at the other end of the scale thyroidectomy at 24 days of age was without significant effect.

Differences in the rank-order of difficulty presented by the several problems involved in this test to normal and cretinoid rats and in the shape of the learning curves have suggested either that different modes of solution are used by the two classes of animal or that some factor is present in the experimental situation which operates differentially against the cretin. It is at present not clear which of these possibilities plays the dominant rôle but if, as has been proposed (Sholl and Uttley, 1953), the nervous system operates in accordance with the principles of conditional probability then a reduction of the probability of interaction between its integrative elements might be expected to give rise to a reduced variability of behaviour resulting from a capacity to respond only to the more dominant features of the environment. This concept implies a predilection for perseverative tendencies and, although this has not so far been examined quantitatively, such tendencies were clearly present in the behaviour of the cretinoid rat in this and other experiments. The presence of opportunities for such perseverative behaviour in one experimental situation but not in another could provide an explanation for some part of the differences between normal and neonatally hypothyroid individuals in the learning and performance of an adaptive response. In this respect it is perhaps of interest that similar perseverative phenomena have been recorded in other circumstances where a reduction of interaction between neurones might be expected; such as, for example, asphyxia neonatorum (through neuronal hypoplasia—Becker and O'Donnell, 1952); nitrous oxide inhalation (through sub-total anaesthesia—Steinberg, 1956); and cretinism in man (Money, 1956).

RECOVERY AS A FUNCTION OF MEDICATION

These experiments thus seem to establish that, in the rat, the influence of thyroid hormone on cerebral maturation is critical during the first few days of life and that thereafter it wanes until by about the tenth day the effects, as tested by the techniques described, are negligible. It remains therefore to enquire how far the success of replacement therapy is dependent upon the age at which this is started.

Attempts to elucidate this problem have tended to give equivocal results. Eayrs and Lishman (1955), using an elevated T-maze, found that medication begun at the age of 25 days was successful in restoring performance and this finding inclined them to the view that, in the rat at least, the effects of early hypothyroidism were not irreversible. By extrapolation, therefore, these results were consistent with the opinion that irreversibility in man might well be due to a superimposed disability of genetic origin. Again, in a more recent study using a conditioned avoidance situation, Eayrs and Levine (1963) likewise found that replacement therapy begun during adult life was successful in restoring the performance of neonatally thyroidectomized rats to normal. In the closed-field test, however, very different results have been obtained (Eayrs, 1961) in which a high positive correlation was found between ultimate attainment and the age at which medication was started. Thus the results of what must be regarded as a more critical test of cortical function yield information which is consistent with the views expressed by Smith, Blizzard and Wilkins (1957), cited earlier, to the effect that, in man, age is a significant determinant of the sequelae of hypothyroidism. Explanations of the different results obtained in the experiments of Eayrs and Lishman (1955) and of Eayrs and Levine (1963) probably reside in the order of difficulty of the problems presented and the relationship which rate of performance bears to the mode of scoring behaviour. Full discussion of the underlying factors is beyond the scope of this communication but the findings serve to draw attention to the importance of methods used for testing and the need for care in the interpretation of data.

INFLUENCE OF NEONATAL HYPERTHYROIDISM

The effects of thyroid excess during the period of cerebral maturation have been little studied and the somewhat unexpected results of recent experiments are therefore worthy of mention. Large doses of L-tri-iodothyronine given to infant rats give rise to acceleration in the appearance of criteria of physical maturation and of landmarks of innate behaviour. When the treatment is given before the fifth day of life growth is retarded and the treated animals continue to grow less well long after the administration of hormone is discontinued. Apparently permanent changes are seen in the pituitary, consisting of an overall hypoplasia associated with a degranulation of acidophils (Eayrs and Holmes, 1964). Furthermore the experimental animals, when examined by the closed-field test, perform significantly worse than do their normal littermates (Eayrs, 1964). These effects do not arise when the treatment is delayed until the 14th day of life.

The causes of these phenomena await elucidation. It is tempting to speculate that the rat passes through a critical period during which the hypothalamo-pituitary-thyroid axis is particularly sensitive to the presence of thyroid hormone, in the same way as the hypothalamic control of the secretion of gonadotropin is sensitive to the presence of sex hormone (Barraclough and Gorski, 1961). The impression is gained that animals subjected to excess in early life become hypothyroid later but this is in need of confirmation. The physiological significance of such findings is at the moment obscure but were it to transpire that the placental barrier was crossed by large quantities of thyroid hormone during such a critical period in man, then the possible effects of maternal hyperthyroidism upon the future status of the child might become a matter for consideration.

CONCLUSION

An attempt has been made to define some of the developmental changes which arise as a result of an experimentally-induced departure from the euthyroid state and to inter-relate the findings derived from neuroanatomical, neurophysiological and be- havioural studies using the rat. Although much more work needs to be done, these findings have helped to clarify some of the uncertainties arising from the results in the clinical field of in- vestigation outlined earlier. It would thus appear that neonatal thyroid deficiency, irrespective of other complicating factors, can give rise to structural changes in cerebral development which can form the basis of mental retardation. Furthermore, although the presence of complicating factors in man cannot be excluded, the age of onset of the disorder and the time at which medication is begun are important factors determining the measure of reversi- bility of this retardation which can be expected; and finally, if it be permissible to extrapolate from rat to man on the basis of the relative stages of cerebral development, a critical period for the influence of thyroid hormone in man would be expected to occur during the later stages of development *in utero*. While these findings reinforce the need for early postnatal treatment, they might equally be regarded as providing a case for antenatal diagnosis.

SUMMARY

In view of the marked and long-recognized effects of neonatal thyroid deficiency on the mental development of man it is surprising how little has been done to elucidate the neurological basis of the disorder. During the past ten years, however, experimental studies using the rat have revealed structural changes which include a reduction in cerebral growth, disturbances in cranioneural relationships, impairment of the growth of neurones and their processes and a modified pattern of vascularity. The causal relationship between these several phenomena remains obscure, but their impact has been examined in terms of the electrical activity of the brain and of behaviour. Electrocortical potentials are increased in duration but reduced in amplitude, the appearance of innately organized behaviour patterns is delayed and the performance of adaptive tasks impaired. An attempt has been made to inter-relate the structural, neurophysiological and psychological findings and to show the extent to which these depend upon the age of onset of thyroid deficiency.

REFERENCES

ALLEN, B. M. (1938). *Biol. Rev.*, **13**, 1.

BARRACLOUGH, C. A., and GORSKI, R. A. (1961). *Endocrinology*, **68**, 68.

BENDA, C. E. (1947). Mongolism and Cretinism. London: Heinemann.

BRADLEY, P. B., EAYRS, J. T., GLASS, A., and HEATH, R. W. (1961). *Electroenceph. clin. Neurophysiol.*, **13**, 577.

BRADLEY, P. B., EAYRS, J. T., and RICHARDS, N. M. (1964). *Electroenceph. clin. Neurophysiol.*, in press.

BRADLEY, P. B., EAYRS, J. T., and SCHMALBACH, K. (1960). *Electroenceph. clin. Neurophysiol.*, **12**, 467.

BECKER, R. F., and O'DONNELL, W. (1952). *J. comp. physiol. Psychol.*, **45**, 153.

BROWN, A. W., BRONSTEIN, I. P., and KRAINES, R. (1939). *Amer. J. Dis. Child.*, **57**, 517.

BRUCH, H., and McCUNE, D. J. (1944). *Amer. J. Dis. Child.*, **67**, 205.

BULLOCK, T. H. (1959). *Science*, **129**, 997.

CLARE, M. C., and BISHOP, G. H. (1955). *Amer. J. Psychiat.*, **111**, 818.

DYE, J. A., and MAUGHAM, G. H. (1929). *Amer. J. Anat.*, **44**, 331.

EAYRS, J. T. (1954). *J. Anat. (Lond.)*, **88**, 164.

EAYRS, J. T. (1955). *Acta Anat. (Basel)*, **25**, 160.

EAYRS, J. T. (1956). *J. Neuropath. exp. Neurol.*, **15**, 93.

EAYRS, J. T. (1961). *J. Endocr.*, **22**, 409.

EAYRS, J. T. (1964). *Anim. Behav.*, **12**, 195.

EAYRS, J. T., and HOLMES, R. L. (1964). *J. Endocr.*, **29**, 71.

EAYRS, J. T., and LEVINE, S. (1963). *J. Endocr.*, **25**, 505.

EAYRS, J. T., and LISHMAN, W. A. (1955). *Brit. J. Anim. Behav.*, **3**, 17.

EAYRS, J. T., and TAYLOR, S. H. (1951). *J. Anat. (Lond.)*, **85**, 350.

FAZEKAS, J. F., GRAVES, L. B., and ALMAN, R. W. (1951). *Endocrinology*, **48**, 169.

GESELL, A., AMATRUDA, C. S., and CULOTTA, C. S. (1936). *Amer. J. Dis. Child.*, **52**, 1117.

HIMWICH, H. E., DALY, C., FAZEKAS, J. F., and HERRLICH, H. C. (1942). *Amer. J. Psychiat.*, **98**, 489.

HORN, G. (1954). *Lancet*, **2**, 1327.

ISENSCHMID, R. (1918). *Frankfurt. Z. Path.*, **21**, 321.

LEWIS, A. (1937a). *Lancet*, **1**, 1505.

LEWIS, A. (1937b). *Lancet*, **2**, 5.

LOTMAR, R. (1933). *Z. ges. Neurol. Psychiat.*, **146**, 1.

McGIRR, E. M., and HUTCHISON, J. H. (1955). *J. clin. Endocr.*, **15**, 668.

MEANS, J. H. (1948). The Thyroid and its Diseases. Philadelphia: Lippincott.

MONEY, J. (1956). *Arch. Neurol. Psychiat. (Chic.)*, **76**, 296.

OSORIO, C., and MYANT, N. B. (1960). *Brit. med. Bull.*, **16**, 159.

RADWIN, L. S., MICHELSON, J. P., BERMAN, A. B., and KRAMER, B. (1949). *Amer. J. Dis. Child.*, **78**, 821.

RAY, R. D., SIMPSON, M. E., LI, C. H., ASLING, C. W., and EVANS, H. M. (1950). *Amer. J. Anat.*, **80**, 479.

SHOLL, D. A., and UTTLEY, A. M. (1953). *Nature (Lond.)*, **171**, 387.

SIMPSON, S. L. (1948). Major Endocrine Disorders. London: Oxford University Press.

SMITH, D. W., BLIZZARD, R. M., and WILKINS, L. (1957). *Pediatrics*, **19**, 1011.

STEINBERG, H. (1956). *Brit. J. Psychol.*, **47**, 183.

TILNEY, F. (1933). *Bull. neurol. Inst. N.Y.*, **3**, 252.

TREDGOLD, A. F. (1929). A Text Book of Mental Deficiency. London: Baillière, Tindall and Cox.

UTTLEY, A. M. (1955). *Proc. roy. Soc. B.*, **144**, 229.

DISCUSSION

Lewis: Is it practicable to thyroidectomize the foetal rat through the mother?

Eayrs: I would say that surgical thyroidectomy is not practicable, for this is an extremely precarious procedure even in the one-day-old rat. I should think it might be done with ^{131}I, but the thyroid in the rat foetus does not begin to function until two to three days before birth. When methyl thiouracil is given to the mother during the later stages of pregnancy the animals are born with goitres, but they behave in precisely the same way as those treated immediately after birth.

Richter: How far can the behaviour of the cretinous rats be explained by saying it is a failure of memory? I ask because thyroxine affects protein turnover or protein synthesis. Current ideas about memory mechanisms also involve the protein turnover and I am wondering whether there is some common basis there. In myxoedema too, memory failure is a characteristic symptom.

Eayrs: In myxoedema the failure of memory is temporary and can be rectified by giving appropriate therapy. A growth process may not be involved there at all. The behavioural phenomena I described could quite possibly be causally related to the anatomical configuration I described, but in fact there is no evidence for believing that there is anything more than a correlation; nevertheless it is reasonable to infer that higher processes of memory need not be involved. The fact that the development of thalamic afferent plexuses is impaired suggests that the animal will not respond critically to environmental inputs to which the normal animal might well respond. It would thus be expected to be less sensitive to its environment and so, although memory in the sense of storage may be affected, this behaviour could also be explained as failure to recognize features of the environment—to notice rather than to remember in the usually implied symbolic form.

With regard to the possible rôle of protein synthesis, I expect you are thinking of H. Hydén's suggestion (1961. *Sci. Amer.*, **205**, 62) of differentiation of the cell membrane beneath the synaptic ending, with the implication that there is a certain specificity of relationship between the two. This is the sort of phenomenon which might well be invoked to explain the mental defects.

Richter: One doesn't have to rely on Hydén's mechanisms. Growth of the dendritic nerve-endings, which does not involve much growth of the cell or organ as a whole, requires protein synthesis, and thyroxine might act through a mechanism of that kind.

Eayrs: There is no doubt whatever that the changes I have demonstrated anatomically must be expressions of failures of protein synthesis. L. Sokoloff and his associates (1963. *Biochim. biophys. Acta (Amst.)*, **76**, 329; *Fed. Proc.*, **22**, 1102) have recently been showing how important is the presence of thyroid hormone for protein synthesis *in vitro*, using the microsomal fractions of the cell. Sokoloff has some further views on particular aspects of protein synthesis in the brain as opposed to that in other tissues. Could you elaborate on that for us?

Richter: S. Gelber, P. L. Campbell, G. E. Deibler, and L. Sokoloff (1964. *J. Neurochem.*, in press) have found that thyroxine acts particularly in the immature brain, apparently by facilitating the transfer of the soluble RNA amino-acid complexes to the ribosomes, and they have shown there is a change, with the maturation of the brain, in the way it works. The stimulant action of thyroxine is greater in the immature than in the adult brain.

Eayrs: This is one of the two positive pieces of evidence of which I am aware for a structural basis for the irreversibility of mental impairment. The other is work by M. Hamburgh and L. B. Flexner (1957. *J. Neurochem.*, **1,** 279) in which they showed an irreversibility of the development of the activity of succinic dehydrogenase.

Richter: The idea that protein metabolism is primarily affected does help a little to explain the effect of thyroxine on the basal metabolic rate of different organs, because Sokoloff and his group have pointed out that it is just in those organs, such as the adult brain, spleen and testis, which rely almost wholly on glucose for their metabolism, that thyroxine has least effect.

Greene: One point I am not happy about is the time relationship in the different methods of extirpating thyroid function. We know, for instance, that surgical thyroidectomy in man lowers the thyroid function immediately. Where ^{131}I is used it has been believed until recently that there was a reduction of thyroid function over the next three months, but we now know from recent reports from several different centres that the reduction in thyroid function may go on over a period of years. A large number of people treated for thyrotoxicosis with ^{131}I, who are euthyroid at three months, may become hypothyroid several years later. In the third method, the use of anti-thyroid drugs, there is a fantastic difference between their effect on the thyrotoxic patient and the normal person. People who have been using anti-thyroid drugs in the treatment of cardiac disease in euthyroid patients have reported that some patients require large doses for two or three months before there is any reduction in thyroid function as judged by any method. I have recently been treating a number of euthyroid patients with large doses of anti-thyroid drugs for an entirely different reason, and some of these people have shown no change in ^{131}I uptake or PBI over a period of six months after the beginning of treatment. One expects with the thyrotoxic patients to see the effect within three weeks anyway. Do the same things occur in the rat, and to what extent were they brought into your consideration ?

Eayrs: We are talking about the use of anti-thyroid measures in quite different contexts. Your concern in therapeutic measures is to convert a hyperthyroid state to a euthyroid state, or, in the last cases you mentioned, to a hypothyroid state, whereas I was trying to produce an athyroid state, so that conditions of over-dosage, apart from their side effects, did not really worry me.

One would indeed expect surgical thyroidectomy to have an immediate effect. If rate of bodily growth is to be regarded as a measure of the effects of total thyroidectomy, one would expect the depression in growth rate to be immediate, but in the rat this is not so: surgically thyroidectomized animals go on growing quite normally, by comparison with their intact littermates, for some time before their growth rate starts to drop off significantly. With regard to radiothyroidectomy, 120 μc ^{131}I destroys the thyroid almost completely. In histological examination afterwards, one finds maybe two or three follicles in the general stroma of the residue, with the parathyroid right in the middle. With methyl thiouracil, using the doses that I was using (4 mg./animal—quite a big dose for an infant rat), it is reasonable to budget for a lapse of three days for the thyroid to be depressed to the athyroid state. The ^{131}I method was therefore much more effective and was associated with a bigger difference in error scores in the maze tests than was the methyl thiouracil method. Again, surgical thyroidectomy at ten days of age caused a decrement in performance, whereas methyl thiouracil treatment at that age did not; in other words the delay with the latter seemed sufficient to pass over what I have come to regard as the critical period for the initiation and reversibility of the behavioural impairment.

Richter: The term thyroidectomy has been used by Professor Eayrs and others for an operation which is done with a chemical agent rather than a knife. Sir Aubrey Lewis has suggested the alternative term "thyroclesis", which appears to be a better word.

Greene: Is anything wrong with "extirpation of thyroid function"?

Richter: Too long!

LONGITUDINAL STUDY OF INTELLIGENCE QUOTIENT IN TREATED CONGENITAL HYPOTHYROIDISM[*]

JOHN MONEY and VIOLA LEWIS

*Johns Hopkins University School of Medicine,
Baltimore, Maryland*

INTRODUCTION: IQ CONSTANCY AND GROWTH

IT is a doctrine of intelligence test construction that the growth of intelligence, in Mental Age units, is by equal annual increments and that the IQ remains, therefore, constant over the years. But tests for IQ are standardized on cross-sections of the population at each age group, not on a single sample followed longitudinally and retested each year. Further, the unit of measurement is on a relative time scale, Mental Age in years, and not on a scale of absolute units. It is like measuring stature in Height Age units instead of inches. Therefore, one does not really know whether, if the growth of intelligence could be measured in absolute units, it would increase by equal annual increments or not. That is, it is not known whether the growth curve for intelligence is a straight line or a curved one showing steep spurts of growth alternating with levelling-off periods.

The problem might be purely academic, should all members of the population grow in intelligence at exactly the same rate, climbing the same growth curve, gaining exactly the same proportional increment of intellectual stature each year. But longitudinal studies (Dearborn and Rothney, 1941; Cornell and Armstrong, 1955; Bayley, 1949, 1955; Sontag, Baker and Nelson, 1958) have shown that such is not the case. For some individuals, the pattern of intellectual growth is atypical, marked by perhaps an eccentric rapid spurt of growth followed by a plateau, or perhaps an eccentric period of decelerated growth. These eccentricities of growth

[*] Research for this paper was supported by Grant No. HD-00325 and Grant No. K3-HD-18,635, United States Public Health Service, and formerly by a grant from the Josiah Macy, Jr., Foundation.

produce, for their duration, an unexpected increase or decrease, respectively, of mental age, and thus a respective elevation or lowering of the IQ.

It is of more than academic interest to know if eccentricities of the growth curve of intelligence might be associated with particular disease syndromes, as are eccentricities of the statural growth curve. One's prognostic skill and predictive power are thereby sharpened.

Congenital hypothyroidism is a syndrome in which the level of intelligence is known to be adversely affected, but it is not known whether the growth rate of intelligence is also affected, especially in relation to treatment. By contrast, it is known that after the institution of thyroid substitution therapy statural growth undergoes a rapid acceleration or catch-up, provided the critical stage of epiphysial fusion has not already been attained. Thereafter, the speed of growth during the remainder of the growing period follows the normal euthyroid pattern.

PURPOSE

The purpose of the present study is to examine the IQs of a group of 43 congenitally hypothyroid patients in a follow-up study, to see whether they remained constant or if any information might emerge concerning trends of IQ change.

SAMPLE SELECTION

The basic criteria of sample selection for this study were a diagnosis of congenital hypothyroidism, a history of thyroid treatment and a subsequent interval of at least five years, with a maximum interval of eleven years between the first and last IQ tests. All of the 43 patients included were being followed or had been followed in the paediatric endocrine clinic of the Johns Hopkins Hospital. Thirty-seven patients in the present study are part of a sample of 60 congenitally hypothyroid patients originally studied and reported by Money in 1956. (They were also included in the tabulations of Smith, Blizzard and Wilkins, 1957.) The 37 patients returned for repeat intelligence testing either because they were on the active follow-up list of the paediatric endocrine clinic from 1961 through the beginning of 1963, or else because they lived within the five-state area surrounding Baltimore and were recalled especially for retesting. There was only one recalled patient who could not return to the clinic. In addition, there were six patients who were not in the original study but who satisfied the criteria for inclusion in this present paper, making a total sample of 43 patients.

PROCEDURES EMPLOYED

Since at the time of retest all the patients were over five years of age, the lower age limit for the Wechsler Intelligence Scale for Children (WISC), it was possible to use either that test or the Wechsler Adult Intelligence Scale (WAIS). There was one exception, namely a grossly defective 27-year-old woman, to whom the Revised Stanford-Binet Intelligence Scale, Form L-M, was given. However, the Stanford-Binet, Forms L and L-M, the Wechsler-Bellevue Intelligence Scale, Form I, the WAIS and the WISC were all used in the original testing, dependent upon the age and mentality of the patient and the availability of the test at the time. The Stanford-Binet tests were used with children from the ages of 2 years to 5 years; the WISC was used with patients from 5 years to 15 years and the Wechsler-Bellevue I and the WAIS with patients 16 years or older, unless their retardation was so great as to require the Stanford-Binet. All the tests were given by three members of the psychohormonal research unit and the majority of retests were administered by the same person. Though the variability of the data is adversely increased when more than one test is used, there was no alternative available under the present conditions of longitudinal study.

Judgments of the age of euthyroidism were obtained from the records of the late Dr. Lawson Wilkins. They were made on the basis of clinical and laboratory findings. Euthyroidism was generally judged to be established three months after the institution of optimum treatment.

FINDINGS

IQ CHANGE

In Table I pertinent data are given to put on record the great diversity in the various relationships between IQ level, IQ change, age of euthyroidism and age of testing for each subject in the study.

TABLE I

INDIVIDUAL IQ CHANGES CLASSIFIED BY AGE AT TESTING AND AGE OF EUTHYROIDISM

I. EUTHYROIDISM ESTABLISHED (3 MO. TO 3 YR.)

A. Age 2 yr. to 7½ yr. at 1st Testing

Hospital Number	Initials	Age 1st Testing	IQ 1st Testing	Age 2nd Testing	IQ 2nd Testing	IQ Change	Age Euthyroid
891940	GB	2–2	100	8–1	105	5	3 mo.
708794	PF	2–6	80	7–11	86	6	4 mo.
883732	DD	5–5	< 60	11–10	54	< –6	4½ mo.
887596	DW	2–11	M. Def.	11–5	< 46	?	4 mo.
888834	MD	2–7	123	9–8	125	2	5 mo.
898150	RW	2–8	81	8–8	83	2	5 mo.
982771	RG	6–2	96	14–8	93	–3	5 mo.
611755	JF	4–3	55	8–11	72	17	6 mo.
897573	BL	4–1	92	12–6	91	–1	6 mo.
964793	KC	5–2	95	14–0	98	3	9 mo.
495760	SO	7–2	79	16–2	83	4	12 mo.
670507	MM	5–1	55	13–3	64	9	21 mo.
888335	BM	3–1	62	11–11	79	17	22 mo.
719619	SB	2–8	72	10–0	59	–13	2 yr.
908825	JL	2–10	103	8–6	96	–7	2 yr.
964150	WB	5–2	84	15–11	128	44	2¼ yr.

B. Age 9 yr. 8 mo. to 24 yr. at 1st Testing

415887	HB	11–6	71	19–7	77	6	10 mo.
741846	GC	20–1	99	29–0	93	–6	12 mo.
948023	RD	14–6	79	23–5	100	21	14 mo.
215879	RS	16–5	42	27–4	52	10	17 mo.
948878	CD	11–4	98	20–5	95	–3	22 mo.
377421	DH	11–11	67	20–6	76	9	3 yr.
744574	LP	10–1	< 46	14–10	< 46	?	2¾ yr.

II. EUTHYROIDISM ESTABLISHED 3 YR. +

A. Age 2 yr. to 7½ yr. at 1st Testing

926854	RH	4–4	67	9–0	73	6	3¼ yr.
767238	LL	3–10	48	9–2	87	39	3½ yr.
552459	PP	7–7	79	15–0	99	20	3½ yr.
601881	DO	3–11	68	10–3	70	2	3½ yr.
609085	GS	4–10	69	14–1	67	–2	5 yr.
748584	WG	6–2	75	12–5	90	15	6¼ yr.
723646	AB	6–5	61	15–0	82	21	6¼ yr.
774815	SJ	7–3	46	16–9	69	23	6½ yr.
663550	CT	7–5	62	14–19	72	10	8¼ yr.

TABLE I—*continued.*

B. *Age 9 yr. 8 mo. to 24 yr. at 1st Testing*

Hospital Number	Initials	Age 1st Testing	IQ 1st Testing	Age 2nd Testing	IQ 2nd Testing	IQ Change	Age Euthyroid
331641	CF	18–2	48	27–7	54	6	4 yr.
368733	RZ	12–10	91	22–5	101	10	4½ yr.
947776	RS	20–10	90	31–8	93	3	6 yr.
501244	BM	11–5	89	20–5	107	18	6¼ yr.
620785	WD	20–0	60	28–11	65	5	6¼ yr.
327863	NA	17–5	64	26–2	78	14	7 yr.
624872	DW	9–8	74	18–0	88	14	9 yr.
749562	DF	13–0	68	17–11	88	20	13¼ yr.
410064	DP	24–1	59	33–0	70	11	19 yr.
566587	ND	15–7	74	25–1	88	14	20 yr.
309094	GMc	20–0	M.Def	27–10	M.Def.	?	not

Figs. 1 and 2 show that the great majority of subjects showed, on final testing, an IQ increase which was often trivial but sometimes very great. The numerical calculations are shown in Table II. These and all subsequent numerical calculations do not include the four patients whose defect was so severe that they could not, on test or retest, be assigned a definite IQ figure.

Clearly, from such statistics, one does not expect that the present findings of IQ gain are a chance happening that will not be replicable. The challenge rather is one of how to explain the change. Are any aetiological or therapeutic variables consistently

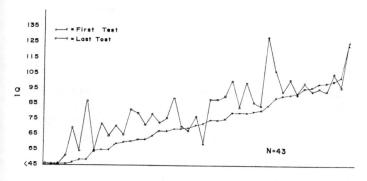

INDIVIDUAL SCORES

FIG. 1. IQ change in congenital hypothyroidism (arranged in ascending order of IQ magnitude at first testing).

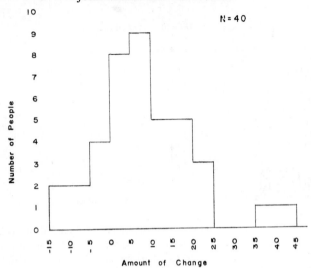

FIG. 2. Frequency distribution of amounts of IQ change in congenital hypothyroidism.

TABLE II

FOLLOW-UP CHANGES IN IQ

	1st Testing	2nd Testing
Mean	75·0	84·5
S.D.	17·8	16·8

$$N = 39$$
$$t = 5·27$$
$$t_{0·001} = 3·55$$
$$P = < 0·001$$

related to degree of IQ change? Is IQ change so multiply determined that no such consistencies can be extracted from the present data? Or, perhaps, is IQ gain, upon retest, simply a reflection of that retest sophistication which has been encountered in other follow-up studies?

IQ GAIN, AGE OF EUTHYROIDISM AND AGE OF TESTING

In Table III one sees that, at the time of first testing, the advantageous effect on IQ of early versus late treatment was statistically

TABLE III

IQ GAIN AND AGE EUTHYROID

	1st Test Euthyroid		2nd Test Euthyroid	
	Before $2\frac{1}{2}$ yrs.	After $2\frac{1}{2}$ yrs.	Before $2\frac{1}{2}$ yrs.	After $2\frac{1}{2}$ yrs.
N	19	20	19	20
Mean	82·4	68·0	88·4	80·8
S.D.	19·4	12·7	19·0	13·3
	$t=2·70$		$t=1·40$	
	$t_{0·01}=2·71$		$t_{0·2}=1·30$	
	$P=$0·02 to 0·01		$P=$0·2 to 0·1 (not significant)	

significant at almost the 1 per cent level of confidence. This advantage had lost statistical significance at the time of second testing, which possibly suggests that a chronological factor of age and/or time elapsed between onset of therapeutic euthyroidism and IQ testing might be responsible. An analysis of variance applied to the 2×2 classification of data in Table I failed to show any statistically significant effect, on IQ gain, of age of euthyroidism and or age of testing ($F = 0·214$ for Euthyroid Age; $F = 0$ for Testing Age; both without significance).

The age effect was further analysed by a threefold subdivision of the data on the basis simply of age at last testing (Table IV).

TABLE IV

IQ GAIN AND AGE WHEN TESTED

	Age tested (years and months)		
	Group I 7–11 to 11–11	Group II 12–5 to 17	Group III 18 to 33
N	11	13	15
Mean IQ gain	6·9	12·5	8·8
S.D.	13·14	12·73	7·04

t-tests:

Groups I and II, $t=1·018$ (not significant)
Groups II and III, $t=0·942$ (not significant)

Analysis of variance again showed the differences between the groups to be not statistically significant. Paired comparisons of the most divergent means also were without statistical significance (Table IV).

One concludes that neither the length or shortness of interval between birth and recognition and correction of hypothyroidism, nor differences in age due to a longer or shorter interval of euthyroidism before the first IQ test bear a linear relationship to IQ gain. Possibly both variables may be alternatives or supplements to one another; or they may both be positive in effect but subject to masking and interference from other factors present in some patients; or they may both be insignificant or secondary in importance to some other factor that influences IQ gain once thyroid therapy is guaranteed.

IQ GAIN AND IQ LEVEL

Table V shows no proportional relationship between amount of IQ gain and the IQ level at final testing.

TABLE V

IQ GAIN AND IQ LEVEL

	IQ 52–73	IQ 76–88	IQ 90+
N	12	13	14
Mean IQ gain	7·00	13·00	8·43
S.D.	8·68	9·70	13·55

Between groups, F=0·958 (not significant)

IQ GAIN AND SEX

Sontag, Baker and Nelson (1958, pp. 37–39) in their longitudinal study found boys more than girls tended to have developmental curves of IQ gain. In the present study, the higher mean IQ gain for boys did not reach statistical significance (Table VI).

OTHER FACTORS AND IQ CHANGE

In the ideal experimental design, one would control the time of foetal or neonatal onset and severity of thyroid deficiency; its origins in athyreosis, goitrous cretinism, enzymic defect, autoimmunization, and so forth; and its duration prior to commencement of hormonal therapy and the first IQ reading. In an

TABLE VI

IQ GAIN AND SEX

	1st Test		2nd Test		Gain	
	♂	♀	♂	♀	♂	♀
N	12	27	12	27	12	27
M	72·8	75·9	86·6	83·6	13·8	7·6
S.D.	17·2	18·0	19·8	15·2	11·23	10·7
	$t = 0·494$		$t = 0·526$		$t = 1·608$	
	(not significant)		(not significant)		(not significant)	
					$(t_{0·1} = 1·684)$	

observational, fieldwork study like the present one, in which many patients have been on treatment for years, it is impossible to make even an approximately complete retrospective classification of patients according to all these variables. To say nothing of the time-consuming labours involved, modern tests that assist in classification are inapplicable, in many instances, after treatment has begun. Consequently, in the present sample of cases, there is an unknown amount of interaction between these uncontrolled variables which is sufficiently complex to preclude their systematic statistical evaluation. Suffice it to say that inspection of the data in Table I and Fig. 3 shows every variety of permutation and combination of time elapsed relative to birthday age, treatment age and testing age, and relative to diagnostic subclassification in cases when it was known.

IQ CURVE CHANGES: INDIVIDUAL EXAMPLES

Fig. 3 shows individual age changes in IQ. An individual graph was drawn for all 19 patients who were tested four or more times. For some of the oldest patients, records were on file in the Division of Child Psychiatry of test results obtained before the present study began. When they were on record, Gesell developmental scores in infancy were used as rough estimates of IQ, in order to show developmental trends before and after early infantile diagnosis and treatment.

The individual IQ graphs, when test results were available before treatment or immediately after, do not show any special tendency for immediate rapid gain followed by IQ constancy. In

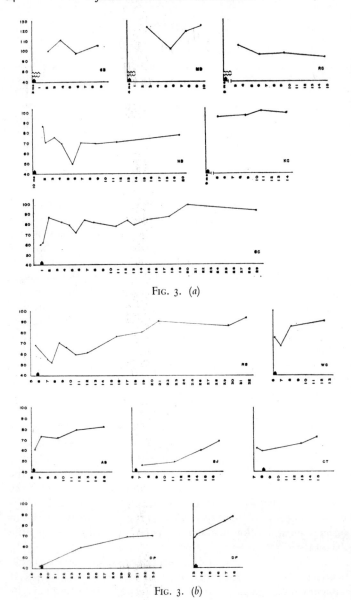

Fig. 3. (a)

Fig. 3. (b)

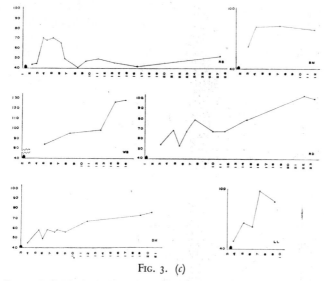

FIG. 3. (c)

FIG. 3. Individual IQ changes in children made euthyroid: (a) before one year of age, (b) from 1 to 3½ years of age, (c) after 3½ years of age. IQs from Wechsler or Stanford-Binet or estimated from Gesell scores according to age.

fact, some show a fall soon after treatment and a subsequent recovery.

Though there is marked individual variability in the pattern of sequential IQs, the commonest characteristic is one of progressive IQ improvement with increasing age, regardless of other considerations. The improvement may extend into adulthood, in the older patients. One cannot systematically relate IQ gain to a particular segment of the recovery period, or to the duration of total or partial thyroid lack.

DISCUSSION

The present study is about IQ gain and does not attempt to isolate the variables responsible for IQ level in hypothyroidism—though there is, of course, some interdependency between the two since IQ gain determines ultimate IQ level, distributed as shown in Fig. 4.

IQ gain was found to be statistically significant in this retest follow-up study. This gain failed to show statistical relationship to the time elapsed before the patient was diagnostically identified and treated, to the time elapsed before the test for IQ, to the IQ level or to sex. The criteria of subdivision applicable to the present data are quite crude, however, and may be masking pertinent

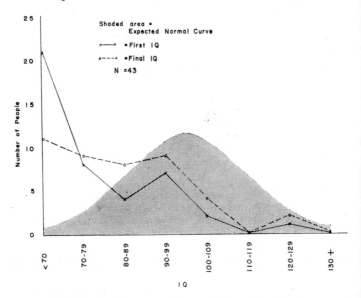

FIG. 4. IQ distribution in 43 cases of congenital hypothyroidism on test and retest.

relationships. For example, there may be a critical period well below the age of $2\frac{1}{2}$ years when the timing of thyroid replacement therapy is of crucial importance. On the basis of inspection of individual data, it was not possible to perceive even a tentative relationship between IQ gain and such a critical period, nor other known diagnostic and clinical facts of each case.

One must consider the improvements of IQ, therefore, simply as a developmental phenomenon. A gain in IQ, upon retest at a later stage of development, may in part represent examination confidence and test know-how that accrues simply from having taken a similar test before. Bayley (1955) has argued cogently that this proposition cannot, however, be used to explain away large changes in IQ. Nor, of course, can it be used to explain the often large IQ losses in the growth studies at Harvard (Dearborn), Berkeley (Bayley) and Fels (Sontag).

In all three of these longitudinal studies it was found that children have different patterns of fast or slow rates of intellectual growth, reflected in growth periods of IQ gains or losses, respectively. Contrary to classic test doctrine, continuing intellectual growth into adulthood was also found, until even as late as the age of 25 years when the Berkeley subjects were given their final test.

The graphs of sequential IQ scores for those subjects in the present study who had multiple retests show the same kind of individual variation that has turned up in other longitudinal studies. By far the most characteristic long-term trend is one of gain. A sequential pattern of increments over the years may be punctuated by temporary losses. Usually the increment of gain is modest, but in some cases there is a sudden leap. One has confidence in the validity of the test results in these latter cases since they were maintained in multiple testings and/or were in keeping with school or vocational achievement. The upper age limit after which gain will level off cannot be specified at present, but it was certainly well into the adulthood of some of the patients.

Prognostically, the conclusion to be drawn is that some treated hypothyroid patients, despite very unfavourable beginnings, will make dramatic improvements in IQ, although others will not; and some will continue to make small IQ increases well into adulthood. The cautious clinician will, therefore, not commit himself to any dogmatic predictions about the distant future of a hypothyroid child's intellect.

SUMMARY

Forty-three patients with congenital hypothyroidism and a history of thyroid substitution treatment were tested for IQ and retested within an interval of at least five and as many as eleven years. The mean IQ changed upward from 75 to 84·5, with standard deviations of 17·8 and 16·8 respectively. The range of IQ change was from −13 to +44, and the distribution of amount of change roughly approximates the normal curve, with the great majority of cases showing a small or moderate gain. It could not be demonstrated that the amount of IQ change related to (1) early versus late age of becoming euthyroid; (2) long or brief interval between age of euthyroidism and age of testing; (3) IQ level; (4) sex; or (5) other known clinical and diagnostic facts. Concerning IQ level itself, there was a tendency, significant at almost the 1 per cent level, on first testing, for patients to have a higher IQ by an average of 14 points if they were made euthyroid before, as opposed to after, the age of $2\frac{1}{2}$ years. On final testing, the average difference fell to 8 points, and statistical significance to between 10 and 20 per cent. Individual graphic representation of sequential IQs, possible in some cases of multiple retesting, showed a variety of IQ gain or loss sequences, consistent with the variety found in other longitudinal studies, and apparently not thyroid-related.

ACKNOWLEDGMENTS

The authors wish to thank Dr. Leon Eisenberg for making available records from the division of child psychiatry and Dr. Robert Blizzard for providing diagnostic data from his thyroid research laboratory.

REFERENCES

BAYLEY, N. (1949). *J. genet. Psychol.*, **75**, 165.

BAYLEY, N. (1955). *Amer. Psychologist*, **10**, 805.

CORNELL, E. L., and ARMSTRONG, C. M. (1955). *Child Develop.*, **26**, 1969.

DEARBORN, W. F., and ROTHNEY, J. W. M. (1941). Predicting the Child's Development. Cambridge, Massachusetts: Sci-Art Publishers.

MONEY, J. (1956). *Arch. Neurol. Psychiat. (Chic.)*, **76**, 296.

SMITH, D. W., BLIZZARD, R. M., and WILKINS, L. (1957). *Pediatrics*, **19**, 1011.

SONTAG, L. W., BAKER, C. T., and NELSON, V. L. (1958). Mental Growth and Personality Development: A Longitudinal Study. Monograph No. 68 of the Society for Research in Child Development (Vol. 23, No. 2). Lafayette, Indiana: Purdue University Child Development Publications.

DISCUSSION

Reeves: Did you break down the results according to the Binet or Wechsler sub-tests, taking into account that some of these tests may be much more affected by retention than others?

Money: I haven't done a really detailed breakdown. I have done it by inspection, making a comparison between verbal and non-verbal sub-tests. I did the same thing, systematically, for tests on patients with Turner's syndrome (Money, J. [1964]. *J. psychiat. Res.*, in press; Alexander,

D., Walker, H. T., Jr., and Money, J. [1964]. *Arch. gen. Psychiat.*, **10,** 337) and found that these subjects have a very marked and statistically significant difference between verbal language ability on the one hand and disability for space perceptual organization on the other hand. They also have a specific disability for a right–left orientation and directional sense. In brief, I have been alert to this type of phenomenon in the hypothyroid children but have found no suggestive evidence of it.

Gibson: Was the development of speech in these children normal?

Money: In general this group is typified by many language abnormalities. It is common to find stuttering, late speech development, and a persistence of baby talk beyond the expected time. There are a few who in the earlier years of life show language disabilities that are slightly like those of brain-damaged patients, but who eventually grow out of them.

Reeves: Are you happy, or unhappy as I was when I tried a small study of myxoedema patients, that the Binet, Wechsler, or any other standard intelligence test, is really tapping the sort of deficit shown in the cretin— or for that matter observable in a myxoedema patient off thyroxine for a brief period?

Money: That is a hard question to answer, except to say that when any better tests come along I am a willing purchaser! I would like to have a lot more tests of specific mental function, instead of these global tests.

Reichlin: How well were the children being treated? Had periodic tests of PBI been made in all of them? Was there a difference between upper middle class children and children from the lower income groups where there might be a difference in adequacy of supervision?

Money: I think that they were all receiving optimum treatment. When the endocrinologists made the estimate of the age at which patients were euthyroid, a few were included who had come to live in the vicinity from elsewhere and who had been undertreated for a period. There is only one patient who, in adulthood, is still being undertreated on the basis of what seems to be her optimum behaviour under treatment. Otherwise I think they were all being maintained at euthyroid level.

Reichlin: But what were the criteria for treatment? The parents of some cretinous children will undertreat them because they become difficult to manage and one has to verify the thyroid status by an objective method in order to be sure.

Money: I don't believe that is so. If one has prepared the parents for the tough task of dealing for perhaps two years with the child who becomes hyperkinetic and almost hyperthyroid in behaviour while clinically euthyroid, then the child seems to grow beyond that difficult period and becomes behaviourally much better. I don't want to give the impression that these children were under a *perfect* system of observation. They were judged euthyroid on the basis of the usual clinical criteria and also on the basis of PBI every time they came in for a check-up. When they were given their most recent intelligence test, they were seen again for a check-up by the endocrinologist and were judged euthyroid then.

Stevenson: Did any of the children develop epilepsy?

Money: I don't recall any cases.

Eayrs: Are your two age groups strictly comparable? Any children who have not been diagnosed before 2½ years, and therefore were not known to be euthyroid till after that time, could perhaps have been very mildly hypothyroid beforehand and escaped the net, whereas those who were found earlier would be expected to be drawn from a population perhaps athyroid or hypothyroid earlier in life.

Money: I attempted to subdivide the group along rational lines in the way you suggest, but it wasn't possible to do anything with these data that way. All I can do is to pick out some cases. For example, a little girl who was a most severe congenital cretin and who had been misdiagnosed elsewhere and left untreated until the age of 4, has made a jump in IQ from 47 to 68, according to the last testing, at school, at age eleven. To my astonishment, her reading achievement was only two years retarded, though arithmetic presented more difficulty. I would have expected her, on the basis of the severity of her condition, to have had an IQ below 46, which is the lowest score on the Wechsler test.

Rollin: Do you subscribe to the thesis which Tredgold supports that there are two types of cretin: the primary ament, who is coincidentally a cretin, and the other type of cretin which you were describing? One would expect, if this thesis is correct, that in the ament there would not be much improvement with thyroid treatment. Clinically, when I worked in this field many years ago, it was a fact that some improved and some didn't.

Money: I don't think there is any evidence to justify that thesis completely. The degree of IQ deficit may be related to the foetal age of onset of thyroid failure and to the concomitant amount of injury to the central nervous system. There are two sorts of cretin, in the sense of those with more and those with less neural impairment, but I am not so sure about two different aetiologies.

Lewis: There are more than two sorts. There are some cretins who without treatment improve spontaneously.

Jellinek: I think this differentiation of types of cretins arises from the work of Sir Robert McCarrison (1908; 1913. *Proc. roy. Soc. Med.*, **2**, 1; **7**, 157) on what he called the "nervous cretins" in the Himalayas, who were children with all the obvious appearance of cretinism, plus a cerebral diplegia. Some French workers supported this by EEG studies: J. Chaptal and co-workers (1956. *Presse méd.*, **64**, 2257) differentiated the ordinary sort of thyroid cretin who had a quiet EEG, with flat waves, from the cerebral cretin, in whom they postulated, as it were, cretinism secondary to damage of the diencephalon, and who had grossly disturbed EEG's

and a lot of spikes and slow activity. There might be some sort of relationship between "good" and "bad" cretins on that EEG basis.

Money: It seems a reasonable hypothesis to me. Unfortunately the
EEG records from the patients in my series were lost.

Eayrs: I wouldn't want to push the extrapolation too far, but the critical
period in the rat occurs between the tenth and the fourteenth days of
post-natal life. Before this, athyroidism will have profound behavioural
effects, and after this it has relatively small effects. This period would
probably correspond to the seventh month or so of intrauterine development in man, so that the really critical effect of thyroid deficiency might be
expected to occur before you ever saw these cases. Provided there was a
sufficient titre of thyroid hormone at that time, you might get a sufficient
brain differentiation to enable the IQ to improve. But the completely
athyroid foetuses would provide your group of non-responding people.
I should have thought this to be a rational explanation.

Reichlin: There may be a difference in the amount of thyroxine which
traverses the placentas in different mothers. Cretinism can be prevented if
enough thyroxine is given to the predisposed mother. Perhaps in some
patients there is enough thyroxine around to allow a degree of normal
development; after birth the child may revert to a total thyroid deficiency
state.

Lewis: How is the predisposed mother recognized?

Reichlin: There are women who have had a series of cretinous children.
When given large doses of thyroid extract they give birth to normal
children. This has been worked on by Beierwaltes and his group at Ann
Arbor (Carr, E. A., Jr., *et al.* [1959]. *J. clin. Endocr.*, **19**, 1).

Harris: What is the PBI content of amniotic fluid?

Money: I don't know of any information about that.

PSYCHOLOGICAL STUDIES IN HYPERTHYROIDISM

S. Artunkal and B. Toğrol

*Department of Pharmacology and Therapeutics,
and Department of Psychology, University of Istanbul*

It has long been known that emotional disturbances accompany disorders of the thyroid gland. The clinical picture of thyrotoxicosis seems to mimic the expression of fear or terror generally described as "crystallized fright". The behaviour patterns of these patients also undergo a change, revealing a restless, irritable personality, with clumsy and quick movements. An experimental study of the behavioural as well as the emotional aspects of this disease, using psychological techniques, should therefore be of interest.

It was the working hypothesis of this pilot study that: (a) behavioural changes accompany emotional disturbances in thyrotoxic patients in all common areas such as perception, learning, memory, motor performance, etc., and (b) these behavioural changes could be measured with objective psychological techniques. It was further hoped that these simple and reliable tools would make psychological assessment of these patients possible and provide measures which could predict the outcome of various aspects of this disorder, so helping the clinician in his tasks of diagnosis and prognosis.

MATERIAL AND METHODS

Twenty female thyrotoxic patients were studied. The mean age was 36 years, with a range of 35 years. They were, on the whole, from the middle socio-economic group with a mixed education level: some had completed the equivalent of a sixth-grade education, some twelfth grade, and some were illiterate. This thyrotoxic group was matched for age, sex, socio-economic status and educational background with normal controls.

The clinical diagnosis of thyrotoxicosis was confirmed in each instance by three laboratory tests: 2- and 24-hr. thyroidal uptake and turnover of ^{131}I, Werner's L-tri-iodothyronine suppression test (1955), and basal metabolic rate.

Psychological examination of each thyrotoxic patient was carried out before treatment, and in ten of these cases after the response to treatment, the time interval varying from 4 to 12 months in different patients. Six patients were treated with ^{131}I alone, three with anti-thyroid drugs, and one patient was treated with anti-thyroid drugs and surgery.

Three groups of 14 different psychological tests were used in the investigation, i.e. tests of (a) reaction time, and of motor co-ordination and ability; (b) simple learning and problem solving; and (c) emotionality and personality. The results of the tests on thyrotoxic patients were compared with those on normal controls, and with their own results before and after treatment.

RESULTS

EXPERIMENTS ON REACTION TIME AND MOTOR CO-ORDINATION AND ABILITY

(1) *Reaction-time experiments.* The apparatus was an ordinary laboratory reaction-time set, the chronoscope measuring time in centi-seconds. After they had become familiar with the nature of the apparatus and its operation, the subjects were given tests of simple reaction time to auditory and to visual stimuli and a third test measuring their discriminatory reaction time to two different visual stimuli. Sixty tests were made on each subject in the following order: 10 auditory, 10 visual, 20 visual-discriminatory, 10 visual, 10 auditory stimuli.

The performances of the patients and normal controls were compared by calculating Fisher's t, using the formula for independent means; they were significantly different, as shown in Table I. Compared with those of the normal controls, the reaction times of the hyperthyroid patients were slower at all levels. The greatest difference between the patients and the normal controls was the discriminatory reaction time to visual stimuli ($P < 0.01$).

Ten of these subjects were retested for their reaction time after treatment. The differences were not significant, except to the simple auditory stimulus ($P < 0.05$).

(2) *Experiments on different aspects of motor ability.* A group of six tests, some with appropriate apparatus and some of the paper

TABLE I

PERFORMANCE OF UNTREATED THYROTOXIC PATIENTS AND OF CONTROL
SUBJECTS IN REACTION–TIME EXPERIMENTS*

Experiments	Untreated thyrotoxic patients (N= 10)		Normal controls (N= 10)			
	Mean	S.D.	Mean	S.D.	t	P
Motor auditory	23·7	6·3	18·9	3·5	2·2	0·05
Motor visual	25·0	7·7	18·0	3·2	2·7	0·02
Visual discrimination	37·0	11·4	23·6	5·3	3·8	<0·01

* Numbers represent time in centi-seconds.

and pencil variety, was used to measure different aspects of
motor ability, including steadiness and precision, accuracy, speed
and endurance in muscular co-ordination. The thyrotoxic

TABLE II

PERFORMANCE OF UNTREATED THYROTOXIC PATIENTS AND OF CONTROLS IN
TESTS OF MOTOR CO-ORDINATION

Experiments	Untreated thyrotoxic patients (N=20)		Normal controls (N=20)			
	Mean	S.D.	Mean	S.D.	t	P
Precision						
Whipple's tracing board	115·32	36·8	144·94	39·8	2·38	<0·05
Paper and pencil variety	96·06	43·2	141·04	38·5	3·40	<0·01
Steadiness						
No. of holes	2·35	1·29	4·85	1·35	5·81	<0·001
Errors	6·69	2·83	2·11	1·0	6·65	<0·001
Motility						
Right hand	28·6	5·7	36·0	4·6	4·45	<0·001
Left hand	24·7	5·7	31·8	5·5	3·92	<0·001
Accuracy	2·48	1·46	2·18	1·33	0·7	n.s.*
Endurance	15·98	4·22	19·97	3·59	3·15	<0·01

* Not significant.

patients were significantly poorer performers in all these tests, except the one for accuracy, than the normal group (Table II). Though there was a small improvement in these tests after treatment, it was not at a significant level.

The fatigue curve for tests of muscular endurance is seen in Fig. 1. The curves for thyrotoxic patients and the normal controls display a qualitatively similar pattern but differ quantitatively,

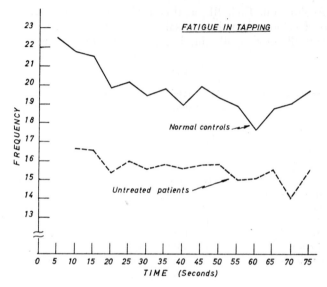

FIG. 1. Fatigue curve of thyrotoxic patients and normal controls in tests of endurance.

defining the patients as poor performers throughout the experiment. They seem to have started their tasks as very tired people, and to have continued to be so the whole time.

SIMPLE LEARNING AND PROBLEM-SOLVING EXPERIMENTS

(1) *Mirror Drawing*. In the mirror drawing experiment, in which the subject learns to trace a pattern while viewing its reversed image in a mirror, the familiar situation where the subject reacts with co-ordinated behaviour to visual and kinaesthetic

cues is altered. A new eye-hand co-ordination which runs counter to previous smoothly working ones must be formed. Rational planning is of little help during early trials, behaviour being reduced to the level of trial-and-error procedure.

The subjects were given five trials for this task. The means of the times taken and the number of errors committed in these repetitions were compared with those of the controls by calculating t.

As shown in Table III, the thyrotoxic patients on the average took less time than the normal controls, the difference being statistically not significant, but they committed more errors

TABLE III

PERFORMANCE OF UNTREATED THYROTOXIC PATIENTS AND OF CONTROLS IN LEARNING TESTS

Tests	Untreated thyrotoxic patients		Normal controls		t	P
	Mean	S.D.	Mean	S.D.		
Mirror drawing (N=20)						
Time	113·41	37·5	126·8	65·9	0·73	n.s.*
Errors	27·54	18·45	13·26	9·68	3·00	<0·01
F Puzzle (N=10)	83·4	56·4	83·3	27·7	0·77	n.s.*
T Puzzle (N=10)	91·8	53·2	59·8	19·9	0·98	n.s.*

* Not significant.

($P < 0.01$). Qualitatively, too, the patients in general did not show very much improvement from one trial to the next, whereas their normal controls improved steadily.

(2) *T and F Puzzles.* In this group of experiments the subjects were given first an F outline and forms to fit into this F, and then the same task was repeated with a T outline. Both the patients and their controls found this a rather difficult task, there being no significant differences in their performances (Table III).

TESTS OF PERSONALITY AND EMOTIONALITY

(1) *Minnesota Multiphasic Personality Inventory (MMPI).* The MMPI was constructed by Hathaway and McKinley (1951) to

provide, in a simple test, scores on all of the more important facets of personality. The test consists of 550 personality items sorted by the patient into true and false categories. The items are scored to yield a profile consisting of four validity scales and nine clinical scales. In the clinical application of the MMPI profiles, the interpretation usually does not rest upon the elevation of a single score but attention is given to the configuration of all the scales in the profile.

In Fig. 2 mean profiles for thyrotoxic patients (before and after treatment) and for normal controls are shown. The thyrotoxic patients both as individuals and as a group show a marked profile type, with a high elevation at the Paranoia (Pa) scale, the mean reaching a T value (see Hathaway and McKinley, 1951) of 80, with two relatively smaller modes at Depression (D) and Schizophrenia (Sc) scales respectively. When the patients and the controls were compared by the χ^2 test in terms of all the above categories, the difference was reliable ($\chi^2 = 18 \cdot 35$; df $= 8$; $P < 0 \cdot 02$).

The profile type of the patients after treatment follows exactly the same outline, the (Pa) scale equalling a T value of 70 this time. The scale for (D) seems to persist at the same value. The differences, however, do not seem to be significant when the χ^2 test in terms of all categories was given to compare the patients' results before and after treatment ($\chi^2 = 2 \cdot 06$; df $= 8$; $P < 0 \cdot 10$).

(2) *The Rorschach Test of Personality.* In the Rorschach test the subject is shown a series of ten ink blots, in themselves meaningless, and is asked to describe what he sees. The scoring of the Rorschach responses is somewhat complex, each response being classified by rigid criteria from different points of view. The clinical psychologist bases his interpretation on the size and proportions of the various scores.

The performances of the patients and the controls in this test were also compared by calculating *t*. The various factors that showed significant differences are shown in Table IV. The most striking difference was the Whole/Movement relationship, the ratio for the patients being very high as compared with the normal ratio.

(3) *Experiments with the Kinephantoscope.* Visual situations can be designed that may call out a large number of different perceptual organizations with about equal probability. Different personality

4*

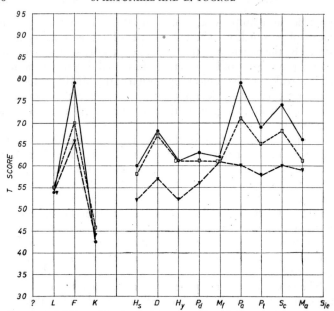

FIG. 2. MMPI profile chart. Mean profiles of thyrotoxic patients before and after treatment, and of normal controls. —●— Untreated patients; --□-- Treated patients; —▼— Normal controls.

TABLE IV

RESPONSES OF UNTREATED THYROTOXIC PATIENTS AND OF CONTROLS IN THE RORSCHACH TEST OF PERSONALITY

Responses	Untreated thyrotoxic patients (N=15)		Normal controls (N=15)			
	Mean	S.D.	Mean	S.D.	t	P
Form(%)	72·0	13·6	59·33	16·21	2·24	0·05
Main total (determinants)	20·26	7·04	31·93	11·09	3·34	<0·01
Total response	19·73	8·64	29·53	9·62	2·82	<0·02
Total time	21	6	24·26	7·55	1·27	n.s.*
Whole/Movement	$\frac{5\cdot06}{0\cdot73}=6\cdot91$		$\frac{4\cdot08}{2\cdot06}=1\cdot98$			

* Not significant.

types differ in their responses to such situations. A device called a *kinephantoscope* (Miles, 1931) consists of a rotating horizontal metal strip which casts a sharply etched shadow on a screen, the visual sequence repeating itself indefinitely, and offering organizations with multiple possibilities. This device was shown to the subjects for five minutes and the numbers and kinds of shifts occurring during this period were counted. On the average, the responses of the thyrotoxic patients compared with those of normal controls were fewer, the *t*-test showing a significant difference for number of shifts, as shown in Table V.

TABLE V

RESPONSES OF UNTREATED THYROTOXIC PATIENTS AND OF CONTROLS IN THE EXPERIMENTS WITH THE KINEPHANTOSCOPE

Experiment	Untreated thyrotoxic patients (N = 10)		Normal controls (N = 10)		t	P
	Mean	S.D.	Mean	S.D.		
Kinephantoscope						
No. of shifts	24·1	9·4	36·1	13·2	2·76	0·02
Kinds of shifts	3·4	0·5	4·4	0·9	1·92	n.s.*

* Not significant.

DISCUSSION

From these tests the conclusion can be drawn that there are statistically significant differences between the performance of thyrotoxic patients and that of their normal controls throughout the experiments. Some of these differences were perhaps to be expected; nevertheless, some rather striking points have emerged.

Throughout the reaction-time experiments, there seems to be a latency in the patients' reaction time to different sorts of stimuli which is rather unexpected from individuals who apparently show a high degree of restlessness in their actions. After treatment there seems to be a shift towards the normal range, the only significant difference being in their reaction time to a simple auditory stimulus before and after treatment (see Table VI).

In tests measuring muscular co-ordination and motor ability, the patients are significantly poor performers for all situations, the differences between their performances and those of the normal subjects being highly significant. This is to be expected, of course, from patients who show a restless and irritable personality, and who have muscular weaknesses and clumsy movements. In all parts of this group of tests, their achievements after treatment did not differ significantly from their performances before treatment. These results deserve further investigation.

The simple learning test introduced by the mirror drawing situation showed a high incidence of errors on the part of the patients. This may indicate an interesting trait concerning these patients, and at this point we should like to draw attention to the results of similar experiments on manipulative simple learning

TABLE VI

Tests that indicate significant differences in the performances of thyrotoxic patients before and after treatment

	t	P
Reaction time: Motor auditory	2·1	0·05
Mirror drawing		
Time	4·35	< 0·01
Errors	2·86	< 0·02
Kinephantoscope	3·05	0·01

processes conducted in primates in relation to lesions in different parts of the cortex (Jacobsen, 1932; Jacobsen and Nissen, 1937). As a result of these experiments, it was found that in primates lesions in motor and premotor areas produce some interference in their performance. This interference was more with the motor skills of the animals than with their learning or memory capacity, where the organization of components of a skilled movement seems to have been impaired. Comparing the results of our simple learning experiments with those of Jacobsen's primates, can we perhaps predict the possibility of a "biochemical lesion" in these regions of the cortex in our thyrotoxic patients? The reliable differences obtained on retesting our patients may, however, be partly due to a latent practice effect ($P = 0·01$ and $P = 0·02$) or perhaps, to a recovery of some sort (see Table VI).

The MMPI test of personality yields an interesting profile for this group of patients, revealing pictorially and in an integrated and quantitative form the personality traits of these patients. Reichlin's (1959) finding that the thyroxine turnover rate was slightly raised in paranoid schizophrenics supports our MMPI findings where the profile had high elevations at the paranoid and schizoid points.

The Rorschach test of personality also shows certain interesting details about these patients, especially the high proportion of (Whole) (W) responses to (Movement) (M) responses: (W/M = 6·91). According to Klopfer and Kelley (1946), "M's are rarely found among children up to 8 years of age (except gifted ones), among subjects with organic brain disease, among subjects with a very rigid constriction, and among subjects of rather primitive mentality." According to the same author a healthy balance is reached "if a person has approximately twice as many W's as M's" (as was observed with our normal subjects: W/M = 1·98).

The results of the kinephantoscope test also indicate a marked degree of rigidity and stereotypy on the part of the patients. Harrower's (1939) findings from her experiments with plain reversible figures, where she showed that individuals with cerebral lesions were less flexible in general and less affected by deliberate stimulus weighing of probabilities, are worthy of note here.

Robbins and Vinson (1960), in their experiments on emotionality and personality with thyrotoxic patients, found significant differences between the performances of these patients and those of normal controls and also those of patients with obsessive-compulsive and schizophrenic reactions; but they found strong similarities between the thyrotoxic patients and patients with organic structural changes in the brain.

In conclusion, we could speculate that thyrotoxicosis, which is a metabolic disease, impairs the psychobiological integration of individuals, causing what may be called "biochemical lesions" in certain areas of the cortex (possibly in the premotor and motor areas) which result in the significant differences between the overall behavioural and emotional patterns of these patients and those of normal controls.

ACKNOWLEDGMENTS

Our grateful thanks are due to Miss Esin Cantez for her assistance in the preparation of this paper.

REFERENCES

HARROWER, M. R. (1939). *Brit. J. Psychol.*, **30,** 47.
HATHAWAY, S. R., and McKINLEY, J. C. (1951). Minnesota Multiphasic Personality Inventory. New York: Psychol. Corp.
JACOBSEN, C. F. (1932). *Res. Publ. Ass. nerv. ment. Dis.*, **13,** 225.
JACOBSEN, C. F., and NISSEN, H. W. (1937). *J. comp. Psychol.*, **23,** 101.
KLOPFER, B., and KELLEY, D. G. (1946). *In* The Rorschach Technique, p. 276. New York: World Book Co.
MILES, W. R. (1931). *Amer. J. Psychol.*, **43,** 392.
REICHLIN, S. (1959). *Arch. gen. Psychiat.*, **1,** 434.
ROBBINS, L. R., and VINSON, D. B. (1960). *J. clin. Endocr.*, **20,** 120.
WERNER, S. C. (1955). *Bull. N.Y. Acad. Med.*, **31,** 137.

DISCUSSION

Richter: G. Feuer and P. L. Broadhurst (1962. *J. Endocr.*, **24,** 127) have compared the thyroid function in rats selectively bred for behavioural differences and found that anxious animals had larger thyroids but smaller amounts of thyroid hormone than normal animals. Since the rat doesn't have anything quite corresponding to the human cortex, its behaviour being perhaps determined more at a lower level, the lesion might be wider than the purely cortical one you suggested, Dr. Toğrol.

Toğrol: That is possible. The activities we were trying to investigate were all concerned with the cortical rather than the subcortical level so we thought that there might be something in the cortical area, which we thought might be called, if not a lesion *per se*, then some sort of a biochemical lesion, a blockage.

Money: A number of these disturbances of performance and general function could perhaps be regarded as examples of a more generalized disturbance of attention span. Did all the patients tend to have the same profile on the MMPI or does your Fig. 2 show a summated profile?

Toğrol: They all tended to have more or less the same, some of them almost exactly following the average profile. I was very sceptical about this test to start with, as you seem to be. I am sceptical about most personality tests, but I think our findings from this test might be helpful in this particular disease.

Spence: The psychological changes vary considerably in hyperthyroidism. There are patients with hyperthyroidism who say they feel quite well; there is no emotional upset, no irritability, nothing except perhaps a little exophthalmos, an enlarged thyroid and a raised PBI. On the other hand, I recall a patient aged 28 who developed thyrotoxicosis, and a month or six weeks after this she developed schizophrenia, according to the diagnosis of my psychiatric colleague. One can't say that the schizophrenia was the direct result of the action of thyroxine. We rather thought that she was a latent schizophrenic and that the thyrotoxicosis triggered off the condition; the condition would probably be triggered off by any other profound illness, such as toxaemia. This patient recovered completely after a partial thyroidectomy, and is still well five years later.

Greene: For the first group Dr. Spence described I have invented the word "benignerer", the opposite of "malingerer".

Toğrol: Such cases were excluded from our series. We wanted to study the standard pattern of thyrotoxicosis before going on to other specific kinds.

Harris: Professor Artunkal, would you think it justified to give thyroxine to normal controls until they were perhaps slightly hyper-thyroid, and then repeat your tests?

Artunkal: Yes, I should think so. We have already designed a new series of experiments exactly as you suggest, whereby we are planning to give thyroxine to normal controls and study their responses. We have also started another set of experiments to study borderline cases, and simple goitre patients presenting anxiety states.

Money: It might be interesting to do the same with a group of hypo-thyroid patients in the period immediately after they are given thyroid. Some patients we have had behave for perhaps a year as if they were hyperthyroid.

Artunkal: We have also tried a few such cases, but the sample is too small to say anything about it yet.

Spence: Do you give those patients the full physiological dose to begin with, Dr. Money, or start off with gentle doses and increase them?

Money: We bring them up to optimum doses within about a month or six weeks.

Jellinek: I have been particularly interested in what happens to some of these people with prolonged hypothyroidism after they have been treated. It is generally assumed that they recover but I have about six patients with very prolonged and quite severe hypothyroidism, who were treated and rendered euthyroid, and who have not improved, or who have deteriorated over the years. What happens in these people? We are told that thyroxine has no demonstrable effect on the brain—or sometimes we are told the opposite. I think no one has shown any direct physiological or biochemical action on the adult brain. Professor Eayrs mentioned one paper (Hamburgh, M., and Flexner, L. B. [1957]. *J. Neurochem.*, **1**, 279), on the effect on succinic dehydrogenase in rats, which states specifically that the effect is no longer noticeable once the rats are more than ten days old. It really applies to neonates where the blood-brain barrier is abnormal. I am quite sure there are some direct actions on the brain to be found, although we are nowhere near them yet. Perhaps the work on protein metabolism by Sokoloff that Dr. Richter mentioned (Gelber, S., *et al.* [1964]. *J. Neurochem.*, in press) might lead somewhere.

What happens in these cases of prolonged hypothyroidism is that they get prolonged ischaemic anoxia. Some of our patients were in fact suspected of having cerebral tumours and were subjected to air-encephalography. One woman who presented with a cerebellar syndrome had an excessive amount of air over the right parietal cortex, which was indicative of some cortical atrophy. Another patient, who presented with Dr. Asher's "myxoedematous madness" and a cerebellar syndrome, showed generalized cortical atrophy, with convolutions about 1 cm. away from the skull vault. A man who had been hypothyroid for about 16 years and was unemployable showed some ventrical dilatation, and another man, who had gone well down the social scale since his illness, similarly showed dilatation of the third ventricle (Jellinek, E. H. [1960]. D.M. thesis. University of Oxford). My suggestion therefore is that there is a second possibility, that is of indirect brain damage in these prolonged untreated cases.

Greene: I have always imagined that that is what would happen. Two or three years ago, however, we had a patient who had been a certified lunatic for 13 years. I expected that she would be in the same condition as a patient who has been subjected for a long time to carbon monoxide or hypoglycaemia and that I would be able to do nothing for her. In fact her recovery was extremely slow, but it was complete. After about six months of high dosage with thyroxine she went back to her husband and family.

Richter: I doubt if it would be right to say that thyroxine has no effect on the adult brain. Certainly we cannot measure its effect on the metabolic rate of the brain as a whole. On the other hand there is a good deal of evidence that thyroxine can affect the functioning of the adult brain. For example, in Gjessing's cases of periodic catatonia, although he could find no evidence of thyroid dysfunction, thyroxine removed the mental symptoms. Again there are schizophrenics who show no evidence by the conventional tests of myxoedema, but who nevertheless benefit from a small dose of thyroxine. There is no doubt that thyroxine affects the cardiovascular system, and an alternative possibility is that it acts on the blood vessels and the blood supply of localized regions of the brain, rather than directly on the metabolism of nerve cells.

Harris: A few years ago experimental evidence from the physiologists indicated that the sex steroids acted on the hypothalamus—mid-brain area. This was contested by biochemists because, amongst other reasons, there was no evidence of any uptake of the steroids by different regions in the brain. However, with the introduction of radioactive oestrogens, R. F. Glascock and R. P. Michael (1962. *J. Physiol.* (*Lond.*), **163,** 38P) have found that there is a definite pick-up of oestrogens in scattered cells in the lateral hypothalamus, and earlier we showed (Harris, G. W., Michael, R. P., and Scott, P. P. [1958]. *Ciba Found. Symp. Neurological Basis of Behaviour*, p. 236. London: Churchill) a direct and local action of implanted fragments of stilboestrol on regions in the posterior hypothalamus. The statement that hormones don't have any effect on the brain should therefore be qualified by reference to the sensitivity of the tests on which the data are based. I should have thought that the clinical evidence was very clear. Excess thyroid hormone can produce dramatic results; deficiency of the hormone leads to myxoedematous madness. In view of the fact that abnormal mental states may occur during the course of thyroid disease and that different regions of the central nervous system accumulate radioactive thyroid hormones (Ford, D. H., and Gross, J. [1958]. *Endocrinology*, **63,** 549; Ford, D. H., Kantounis, S., and Lawrence, R. [1959]. *Endocrinology*, **64,** 977) the simplest explanation would seem to be that thyroid hormones exert a direct action on central neurones. They may of course produce irreversible changes.

Mandelbrote: We should be very careful, in talking about thyroid disorders and the psychosis that may occur in either the hyperthyroid or the hypothyroid case, not to think of this in terms of a 1:1 relationship. One doesn't usually get improvement of psychiatric disorders merely by restoring the endocrine balance but rather by using the traditional methods of treating psychosis, irrespective of hormonal change. One case I have seen recently perhaps emphasizes this point. A woman who had a definite hypothyroidism and who had been treated sporadically with thyroxine presented with a schizophrenic psychosis. She was treated with thyroxine in adequate doses, which didn't particularly affect the schizophrenic psychosis, and then she was given chlorpromazine, which presumably would damp down thyroid secretion and which in fact controlled the schizophrenic disturbances. Professor Harris has measured TSH values in this patient and they were very low the whole time, although the psychosis subsided quite adequately. There may have been a tendency to make too much of the 1:1 relationship between the hormonal disturbance and the psychosis.

Jellinek: It is fiendishly complicated. I used to think that the EEG might help: if there is a direct effect of thyroid on the brain one would expect to see some change in the production of brain waves. Most cases with hypothyroidism show quite marked slowing of alpha activity and various other things and in extreme cases you can get an almost completely flat EEG, with hardly anything at all (Nieman, E. A. [1958]. M.D. thesis. University of Liverpool). Again, it is by no means a direct or invariable relationship. The case I described, of a man with myxoedema who had a dilated third ventricle and was grossly retarded, had a completely normal EEG; and I can produce an almost flat EEG for somebody who was only moderately myxoedematous. So I am sure the hormone acts at various levels, directly on those brain metabolisms which we can't measure at the moment, and probably indirectly via the cardiovascular system (Jellinek, 1960, D.M. thesis. University of Oxford).

Reichlin: Dr. Toğrol, would you mention again those abnormalities which seem to persist when the hyperthyroid state is treated?

Toğrol: The patients did not seem to recover significantly in their responses to three of the reaction-time tests, although they did improve in the fourth (auditory stimulus); similarly, their responses to the complete set of tests of motor co-ordination and motor ability did not recover significantly. Their MMPI scores did not show any significant improvement either. They did improve, however, in the simple learning situation but this might have been due to a latent practice effect rather than to recovery.

Reichlin: Do you believe that there appears to be a characteristic pattern of psychological abnormality in Graves' disease even when the patients are not toxic?

Toğrol: Not exactly. All I could say is that those disorders seem to persist even after the physiological treatment has been completed. For those patients who have had several re-testings over a span of several months and/or years we should be able to make a definite statement, but unfortunately we are not in that position yet.

Reichlin: How did you select the control group for your patients? The patient, besides being thyrotoxic, is a sick person, and the precise construction of the control group becomes very difficult.

Toğrol: We have only had normal controls in our experiments and they were exactly matched with our patients in intelligence, age, sex, social background and outlook. It was quite a mixed group, including housewives, maids, university graduates and students, etc., as the cases required.

Spence: If a person is ill with some other serious disease or an infection, would they not give similar results to those of the hyperthyroid patients?

Toğrol: I do not think so, but I cannot be too certain. The only other groups I have worked with were a small group of hypothyroids and another group of male hyperthyroids.

Mandelbrote: We did a somewhat similar study to yours, Dr. Toğrol, of 25 thyrotoxic patients who presented at the endocrine clinic (Mandelbrote, B. M., and Wittkower, E. D. [1955]. *Psychosom. Med.*, **17**, 109). We had the same problem of deciding what sort of controls to study and we decided to study a group of 25 hospital patients. We excluded all the conditions that have been described as being psychosomatic, and the controls had had either surgical operations or medical illnesses. Our study was also concerned in part with an attempt to assess personality make-up, personality traits and personality difficulties. We found that both the control and the thyrotoxic groups showed a fairly wide area of disturbance along these various continua, which are very difficult to measure. We used the Saslow scale to attempt to measure the disturbances in the paranoid sphere and the hysterical sphere. These traits were no more marked in the thyrotoxic subjects than in the controls, and in fact it is the depressive and anxiety continuum which seems to show the greatest disturbance in this comparison. The two sets of people you used might have some relevance to the conclusions drawn. What did stand out in our study was the presence of neurotic and personality problems, which were statistically more significant in this group of thyrotoxic patients than in the group of controls.

Many of these people, although they had been rendered euthyroid, remained as ill people, in different ways. Our sample was obviously biased in that we were studying people who presented at the endocrine clinic. But quite a number of these people were the bane of the endocrinologists —the surgeons had discarded them long ago and they were attending medical out-patient clinics for a variety of other complaints although they were euthyroid. This substantiated one's impression that a number of the people who develop thyrotoxicosis have psychiatric problems which in some cases may be more prominent once the thyroid is rendered euthyroid. Psychiatric treatment resulted in marked improvement in some patients who previously had been chronic invalids. These thyrotoxic patients tended to deny their symptoms, and their basic difficulties were substantially more than those of other groups—at least that was my impression.

Greene: Thomas Dunhill used to say that thyrotoxicosis was a disease which usually attacked poor material.

Money: Psychiatric symptoms in hyperthyroid children seem to be benign as compared with those in teenagers and adults. Also, in a series of 20 children I saw only one with possible psychogenic factors in the aetiology. She was a girl of around three years of age, whose onset of hyperthyroidism was clearly associated with a difficult life circumstance, the death of her father after prolonged cancer. I understand both from the literature and from the people working on adult endocrinology at Johns Hopkins that the incidence of onset of hyperthyroidism in close proximity to stress circumstances in adult life would be more frequent than that. Incidentally, I haven't seen any psychosis in the hypothyroid children either.

Mandelbrote: In our series of 25 patients none had had a psychotic episode at any time, but all of us who work in psychiatry have seen psychoses associated with thyrotoxicosis and hypothyroidism. It is very difficult to say what the direct relationship is between thyroid dysfunction and psychosis. Certainly a substantial number of patients with thyrotoxicosis had encountered life situations which represented a sudden disturbance of a cardinal interpersonal relationship (described previously by Lidz). It seems as if a sudden rupture of a close emotional bond was relevant in time to the onset of thyrotoxicosis.

Stevenson: I would agree with that, Dr. Mandelbrote, but I think that the thyroid has to be considered as in homoeostasis with the other endocrine glands and if there is disturbance in the thyroid, there is consequent disturbance in the hormone equilibrium everywhere. From my experience I felt the disturbance was an attempt at adaptation. I would draw a parallel between the unfortunate experience of diabetics when their blood sugar level, which they have got used to and which has become normal for their mental functioning, is suddenly medicinally lowered to the physiologist's normal, leaving them relatively hypoglycaemic (Stevenson, W. A. H., et al. [1959]. Unpublished work). Too rapid a therapeutic restoration of hypothyroidism to a physiological euthyroidism could surely similarly disturb the adaptation of the patient and render him more liable to break down under environmental stresses instead of adapting to them.

We had cases of psychosis which seemed to follow a definite personality pattern, but there were no hard and fast rules. I would say that children are much more adaptable and malleable to situations than the adult is, and possibly therefore they are better able to adapt while the abnormal thyroid function is being corrected.

I believe it was Charcot who first noted peripheral thyroid insensitivity and one form of that is perhaps interesting. My colleagues, C. P. Haigh, M. Reiss and J. Reiss (1954. *J. Endocr.*, **10**, 273), had a set of patients whom they called pseudo-hypothyroid in whom the ^{131}I uptake curve in the first hour was extremely flat, similar to that of very hypothyrotic patients, but they would pick up gradually so that their 24-hour ^{131}I-uptake rate would be normal, and in some it even became normal when the first observation was prolonged beyond 30 minutes. It was thought that this incongruity could be due to vasoconstriction affecting the thyroid vessels, and in fact when these patients were given ergotamine tartrate and retested the incongruity was normalized.

As I said before, I feel that it is essential to look at the whole picture with the thyroid as just part of it; if the thyroid is disturbed the whole chain of the endocrine system is upset and has got to get over it as well, and psychophysiologically, if I dare use the word, the patient is much less able to cope with stresses and strains and will tend to break down.

One final point: is not the brain a peripheral organ as far as the thyroid is concerned? When we get these cases, some of which react to medication and some of which do not, surely the cause may be intracellular enzyme problems or vascular problems, just as in other parts of the periphery acted on by the thyroid? Has tri-iodothyronine been tried instead of thyroxine? I have heard that tri-iodothyronine works at the intracellular level.

Greene: That is in doubt.

Harris: Tri-iodothyronine, according to Ford and Gross (1958, *loc. cit.*, p. 105) and Ford, Kantounis and Lawrence (1959, *loc. cit.*, p. 105), is accumulated by certain hypothalamic cell groups just as thyroxine is. It localizes in the paraventricular nucleus and the supraoptic region.

Eayrs: Tri-iodothyronine, though more potent, has a biological half-life in the rat of a mere nine hours, as opposed to 20 hours or so for thyroxine, so that tri-iodothyronine would have to be given more frequently to avoid wide fluctuation in the thyroid state. So it has a disadvantage from that point of view, though from the point of view of its biological activity it may represent a later stage in the metabolism of thyroxine.

Reichlin: Dr. Toğrol, the mental disturbances at the extremes of thyroid disease are commonly deliria, both in myxoedema and in hyperthyroid states—deliria which are comparable in many ways to other toxic states of infection and drug poisoning. Did you compare your results from hyperthyroid subjects with those from cases with an organic brain syndrome?

Toğrol: I have not, but L. R. Robbins and D. B. Vinson (1963. *J. clin. Endocr.*, **20**, 120) have. They used three different psychological tests to measure the emotional responses of thyrotoxic patients and found the performance of untreated thyrotoxic patients to be significantly different from that of normal controls, patients with somatization reactions, obsessive-compulsives and schizophrenics, but strongly similar to that of patients with organic structural changes in the brain.

Reichlin: Robbins and Vinson's data have challenged the concept of a psychosomatic aetiology of Graves' disease. They found that all the psychological abnormalities reverted to normal in time, after treatment. Of course this is important, because of the long-standing clinical question: is the personality of the thyrotoxic patient truly disturbed? Is it true that, "once a thyrotoxic, always a thyrotoxic", regardless of the thyroid state?

Toğrol: We do not know yet. As I mentioned earlier, we might be able to answer this question in the future, when we complete our follow-up studies. The controls that Robbins and Vinson have used with organic structural changes in the brain included three cases with avitaminosis, three with cerebral arteriosclerosis, three with post-traumatic encephalopathy, and one cerebrovascular accident victim.

Florsheim: I am surprised that Dr. Reichlin is surprised at the statement, "once a thyrotoxic, always a thyrotoxic". After all, clinical treatment does nothing to the disease; one tries to limit the output of the thyroid gland, but beyond that one has not changed any condition that drove the thyroid to oversecrete in the first place.

Reichlin: I am surprised that you are surprised that I am surprised, because what was once a very obvious simple explanation for Graves' disease is now quite confused. Is thyrotoxicosis due to excessive TSH, or to an abnormal activator having nothing to do with the hypothalamus or the pituitary gland? Are all the nice physiological studies on TSH regulation totally irrelevant to the aetiology of Graves' disease? These are questions which have to be faced now in view of work with LATS (late-acting thyroid stimulator). The studies of Professor Artunkal and Dr. Toğrol are very pertinent. If they can define a true psychic abnormality which persists long after therapy and after the patient has resumed a normal state of life, this supports the psychosomatic aetiology. But from the studies of Robbins and Vinson even this point is controversial.

Brown-Grant: In thyrotoxic patients who have been rendered euthyroid, Ingbar (Ingbar, S. H., and Freinkel, N. [1958]. *J. clin. Invest.*, **37**, 1063) has reported another persistent abnormality—a sustained increase in the rate of thyroxine turnover; he also found an abnormally high rate of turnover in some euthyroid relatives of some thyrotoxics (Ingbar, S. H., *et al.* [1956]. *J. clin. Invest.*, **35**, 714). What is your opinion of these reports?

Reichlin: I have not studied this question personally. However, the work on thyroxine turnover in thyrotoxic patients was repeated by K. Sterling (1958. *J. clin. Invest.*, **37**, 1348), who could not confirm Ingbar's study. Sterling has not, however, studied the relatives.

Harris: If the personality characteristics of thyrotoxic patients remain long after the patients become euthyroid, how would one distinguish whether this was due to some irreversible change that had occurred during the thyrotoxic state, or whether it was an initial characteristic of the patient before any thyrotoxicosis occurred? If it was discovered in siblings who had never been thyrotoxic, that would be a strong indication that it was due to the genetic make-up.

Lewis: Part of the difficulty lies in the choice of control material. I think that a group of anxious patients, free from any physical disease, would possibly yield results of the same sort as have been reported by Dr. Toğrol, and this would be more relevant than a comparison with people with cerebral damage.

Reichlin: One does see more anxiety in thyrotoxic patients than in normals, but one also sees a similarity to the toxic syndromes—disorientation, poor memory, reduced attention and the like.

Lewis: I think all those could be found in patients with severe anxiety. The only psychological test you used which might be expected to show cerebral damage was the Rorschach, wasn't it, Dr. Toğrol?—and we know how anxious patients behave on that.

Toğrol: No, not only the Rorschach. The results of the kinephantoscope test, the mirror-drawing test, and the complete set of reaction and motor co-ordination tests all seem to indicate some sort of cerebral damage. Also, we do know how patients with brain lesions behave in these situations.

Richter: Is there any evidence on the incidence of thyrotoxicosis in different ethnic groups? It is said that in this country the incidence is particularly high in South Wales, and that is partly a Mediterranean population, as judged by the blood groups.

Florsheim: This would be rather hard to interpret. I was told that Los Angeles has a much higher incidence of new thyrotoxic patients than the

Boston area, but they are both part of the same shifting population and it would be very difficult to separate ethnic from geographical effects.

Greene: South Wales is a goitrous area and thyrotoxicosis does turn up more frequently in a goitrous area than in a non-goitrous area. But the majority of the people with goitres in South Wales have not got thyrotoxicosis.

Brown-Grant: Could the higher incidence of detected thyrotoxicosis be related to the fact that in a goitrous area doctors automatically look at the necks of all their patients?

Greene: That comes into it. I am quite sure, for instance, that the doctors around New End Hospital in Hampstead look at their patients' necks much more often than doctors in general, and the incidence of thyrotoxicosis there is enormous.

Mandelbrote: What is the current view about the genetic aspects? When we were doing our study on thyrotoxic patients we found that the incidence of histories of thyrotoxicosis in their relatives was substantially higher than in the control group. Certainly this has been suggested in the literature.

Greene: There is no doubt that there is a strong familial incidence, but I haven't any information that would satisfy the geneticists.

Spence: Nearly 40 years ago (1928. *Ann. intern. Med.*, **2**, 553) A. S. Warthin said that people were born with a Graves' constitution (or the Graves' diathesis) and consequently developed the disease; if they were born without the diathesis they did not develop Graves' disease.

Harris: Epidemics of thyrotoxicosis have been reported in the past, including one in Denmark shortly after the war. Have such reports been substantiated?

Greene: I think it is a fact. The explanation is usually put down to stress, but it didn't happen in Norway, which acted as a control.

Reichlin: Norway was on low rations, and the countries in which the epidemics occurred were on reasonably good rations. According to K. Iversen (1949. *Amer. J. med. Sci.*, **217**, 121) there has to be both stress and reasonably good food to produce the syndrome.

The Los Angeles incidence Dr. Florsheim mentioned could be called an epidemic in a way, because the increased incidence in Los Angeles is perhaps largely due to thyrotoxicosis in former German concentration camp victims who were in hospital there (Weisman, S. A. [1958]. *Ann. intern. Med.*, **48**, 747). This was a curious finding and of course the same ethnic group is represented in the Los Angeles area without a similar incidence of thyrotoxicosis.

Florsheim: My statement was based on the comparison of two U.S. Veterans Administration Hospital populations in Boston and in Los Angeles and the observation was made by Dr. Joseph F. Ross, who was associated with both.

Jellinek: Another point is the question of temperature. In the tropics patients are more likely to complain of thyrotoxicosis than of myxoedema, and this may apply to Boston and Los Angeles as well. I have asked Indian postgraduates about the incidence of myxoedema in India and they made out that it is very low, but they do see the severe cases. In our descriptions we probably include a lot of mild cases which wouldn't be included in a series from India.

Rollin: My impression, which I haven't submitted to any clinical investigation, is that there is no such thing as a hyperthyroid type. If I were asked to go amongst a community of a thousand people and predict which ones were going to develop thyrotoxicosis, I would not even begin. Would any of my colleagues here take on this challenge?

The other question is what sort of person develops myxoedematous madness? We have seen quite a few at New End Hospital and some, as Dr. Greene has described, have been sufficiently fortunate to respond— why I don't know—to adequate thyroid treatment; but there have been others I have followed now for eight or ten years who have improved up to a point and then have stopped. One woman has been restored to a point where she can function as a district nurse, but she is still a very odd character. She is paranoid and she may even be hallucinated. There has been no material difference in her psychiatric state now for six years.

Greene: They certainly don't always get well.

Recognition of the thyrotoxic type seems to me to depend on a frightfully vague clinical impression. I think there are two quite distinct "thyrotoxic types"; one of them isn't really a thyrotoxic type at all, but is physically perfectly normal though excitable. The other one is excitable, fatiguable, irritable, has a large number of apparently thyrotoxic symptoms, but no physical signs, and has normal tests of thyroid function. A few of those people come back again several years later with definite thyrotoxicosis. If there is a thyrotoxic type, I think that is it, but they are not very common in my experience.

Spence: I have seen the same type and I call them "anxiety states". Their thyroid function tests have all been normal and then one sees them six, twelve, or eighteen months later with true hyperthyroidism.

Greene: Now I always write at the end of my report to the doctor: "I think this is the sort of patient who might become thyrotoxic."

Jellinek: About the thyrotoxic personality, I have always assumed that thyrotoxicosis is often a self-limiting disease. If you leave people untreated the majority of them recover, don't they, or may become myxoedematous?

Greene: A lot of them die of heart failure.

Gibson: The thyroid glands of thyrotoxic patients who have been rendered completely euthyroid remain in an unstable state physiologically.

I have seen a patient who was admitted to hospital in a severe depressive state, in whom the PBI fluctuated markedly, although clinically the patient was euthyroid (Gibson, J. G., and Willcox, D. R. C. [1957]. *J. psychosom. Res.*, **2**, 225, Case 5).

Could some of the personality disturbances seen after the treatment of thyrotoxicosis be explained in terms of learning theory ? One would think thyrotoxic patients might condition rather easily, and the persistence of some features regarded as personality traits might in fact be learned responses rather than essential manifestations of personality.

Stevenson: If you regard hypnosis as a form of conditioning, thyrotoxic patients are very difficult to hypnotize.

Money: W. H. Gantt and W. Fleischmann (1948. *Amer. J. Psychiat.*, **104**, 673) reported beautiful results from one patient who showed greatly retarded ability to establish a conditioned reflex, but this ability improved in a clearly demonstrable way week by week as treatment was given. This report illustrates a very valuable experimental method for studies of both the hypothyroid and possibly the hyperthyroid patient.

INDEX*

* Index compiled by Mr. William Hill.